Succeeding as a Maths Teacher

CW00953695

Succeeding as a Maths Teacher

**CAROLINE KENNEDY,
AMIE MEEK, EMMA WESTON AND
JEMMA SHERWOOD**

BLOOMSBURY EDUCATION
LONDON   OXFORD   NEW YORK   NEW DELHI   SYDNEY

BLOOMSBURY EDUCATION
Bloomsbury Publishing Plc
50 Bedford Square, London, WC1B 3DP, UK
29 Earlsfort Terrace, Dublin 2, Ireland

BLOOMSBURY, BLOOMSBURY EDUCATION and the Diana logo are
trademarks of Bloomsbury Publishing Plc

First published in Great Britain 2023 by Bloomsbury Publishing Ltd

This edition published in Great Britain 2023 by Bloomsbury Publishing Ltd

ISBN: PB: 978-1-8019-9205-3; ePDF: 978-1-8019-9203-9;
ePub: 978-1-8019-9206-0

2 4 6 8 10 9 7 5 3 1 (paperback)

Typeset by Newgen KnowledgeWorks Pvt. Ltd., Chennai, India
Printed and bound in the UK by CPI Group Ltd, CR0 4YY

MIX
Paper | Supporting
responsible forestry
FSC® C013604

To find out more about our authors and books visit www.bloomsbury.com
and sign up for our newsletters.

Dedication

There are lots of people that have made this book possible by letting us watch them teach, by getting involved in coaching and mentoring, by guiding and directing us over our careers, by writing and sharing amazing resources, and through discussions about teaching mathematics. Thanks to the superb mathematics education community.
This book is dedicated to Claire Clay, the (not-so) silent contributor, whose passion for calculators is unparalleled, whose knitting is sublime, and without whom we'd never get the meetings titled.

Contents

Introduction 1

1 Planning learning, not lessons 5

2 Some practicalities of classroom instruction 33

3 Responsive teaching 67

4 Representing mathematics 89

5 Reasoning and problem-solving 119

6 Enrichment inside and outside the classroom 147

7 Applying science and research to teaching mathematics 171

8 Personal professional development 197

9 Understanding curriculum and assessment 217

10 Developing your team 239

11 Some practicalities of leading a department 257

References 281

Index 291

Introduction

What's the point of this, anyway? Anyone who has spent any time in the maths classroom has heard that question. We are told that maths is important, that's it's useful, but in the middle of solving an equation it might not necessarily feel that way. The thing is, mathematics has a hugely important place in schools and part of this is due to its utility. A basic level of numeracy is useful in daily life, when you are shopping or making dinner, and statistical literacy allows you to be a critical consumer of marketing and news. Mathematics underpins scientific discovery, economic analysis, computer science and technological development. It's no stretch to say that the modern world is built on mathematics and that people successful in school mathematics have their pick of next steps.

But utility is not where the point of mathematics ends. One of the oldest intellectual pursuits in the world, people have studied mathematics for thousands of years as a part of philosophy or in its own right, appreciating the particular insights that only seem to come from numbers and geometry. If a school curriculum is deliberately broad, to allow pupils to experience the spectrum of human endeavour and thought, then the mathematical lens must be included as it reveals an aspect of truth that cannot be found elsewhere. Rational thought is underpinned by mathematical principles. As the realm of logical deduction, studying mathematics allows pupils to think in ways different to those in history, or music, and allows them to communicate differently. So we see that mathematics must be a fundamental part of a broad, comprehensive education.

Yet there is one more thing that makes the study of mathematics important. There is joy to be found in solving puzzles or problems. There is a kind of thrill in following a set of steps through to a logically flawless conclusion. To those willing to look for it, mathematics has an inherent beauty to rival the greatest art or poetry. Not all pupils will see this, but all pupils should be given the chance to and, with that in mind, we turn our attention to this book.

If you have bought this book you are probably already with us: maths is important and it's fabulous and everyone should experience that. But how do we translate all our good intentions into actions that have the greatest positive effect on our pupils? How can we, practically, achieve all those ideals that we have about a successful education? Those are the kinds of questions we look at throughout the book. This is not a book on theory, nor is it a clarion call to a vocation. It is our attempt to distil years of experience – in the classroom, leading mathematics departments, training and coaching teachers – into something that gives you a focus and a starting point for what we think is the greatest profession in the world.

Reading this book

Succeeding as a Maths Teacher is written roughly chronologically, with the information you need in your earliest years at the start, right through to the time when you find yourself leading a department or responsible for developing the practice of others.

We don't expect that you would read it in one go – although you're very welcome to do so! – rather we imagine that you would keep picking it up and using it as a reference and as a signpost. We direct you to further reading on every chapter so that you can explore whatever takes your interest when you are ready to.

Everything in this book has come through discussion and debate amongst the four of us and while each chapter has a lead author, we decided to present it as a collaborative whole, as it would be impossible to separate our thinking clearly. This means what you read comes from all of us – what we have been taught, what we have observed and reflected on, what we have read and assimilated and tested and refined. It cannot possibly be comprehensive, however. If we haven't said something it's not because we don't think it's important, just that it would be impossible to talk about everything a great teacher would know in one book. Similarly, it is impossible to isolate the origin of everything we talk about here. We have referenced people wherever we were aware of the reference, or could find a reference, but some ideas are an inevitable combination of years of being in the mathematics education community.

Learning your craft

Every one of us, with practice and reflection, can learn more and get better. Teaching is an evidence-informed craft – we can learn from the evidence but ideas live or die in the way we use them, in the culture and habits we create in our classroom, in the attitudes we promote with our actions and our very way of being.

Your teaching craft will evolve over time and we hope that this book will help you along your journey, serve as an overview of important ideas that will take on new meanings throughout your career, and signpost you to plenty more reading and learning whenever you need it.

Caroline Kennedy, Amie Meek,
Emma Weston and Jemma Sherwood
April 2023

1

Planning learning, not lessons

You may be wondering about the title of the first chapter, *Planning learning, not lessons*. We think it's the most important place to start this book, because the most important thing to remember when teaching mathematics is that every decision you make about your teaching should come from thinking deeply about how pupils *learn* mathematics. Learning comes first and planning for it is the backbone of our practice.

A lesson is an arbitrary unit of time. In some schools it's an hour, in others two, in others 50 minutes. Learning topics does not conveniently fit into the lesson time that we have, and it is impossible to know in advance how your class will respond to the learning that you plan. You might find that pupils grasp certain ideas more quickly or slowly than you anticipated. If you have carefully planned a task to expose pupils to multiple aspects of a concept but stop before it is completed because 'time's up', the pupils will miss important learning. When we plan lessons, rather than learning, time becomes the dominating factor influencing our activity. When we plan sequences of learning in a continuum and treat the end of the lesson as the rest break before picking up again, we put the learning first.

In this chapter, we give an overview of the things we should think about when planning; many of these ideas will be explored more deeply in later chapters. We begin with the ethos that underpins a successful department: collaboration.

Collaboration

In an ideal world, all the teachers involved in teaching a topic would come together and work collaboratively to plan it. The advantages of a collaborative approach are immense as there is a wealth of experience in every mathematics department. Different teachers have different strengths: deep subject knowledge; experience; enthusiasm for new ideas; keen interest in different ways of working; experience of primary or A level teaching; and so on. They will have worked in different schools in different parts of the country or the world. This treasure trove of knowledge should be drawn on by all.

It is useful to note that collaborative working is not the same as cooperative working. These are often seen as interchangeable but there is a subtle difference between them that has a monumental difference in process and outcomes. Collaboration is a process of negotiation, decision-making and alignment, whereas cooperation is sharing out the tasks in a project. In teaching, cooperative working usually looks like: 'You do lesson 1 and I'll do lesson 2'. It shares the workload (always a bonus!) but leads to disjointed progression through the learning sequence and none of the rich, developmental conversations that lead to deeper pedagogical understanding, better classroom practice and improved outcomes for pupils.

Collaborative planning develops our pedagogical understanding, increases teacher confidence and improves morale. It is a process that happens over time. Time should be put aside and dedicated for teachers to bring their ideas, share their previous experiences, make suggestions and listen to each other. There should be opportunities for teachers to research how others have approached the topic and which tasks and models would be most useful. They should think about shared language, common approaches and misconceptions they have encountered frequently.

The main barrier to this process is that scarce and precious commodity: time. Learning-focused leadership teams should designate directed time to plan together, but if you don't have this, make mathematics conversations part of your daily interactions with colleagues. Education happens in a community and must be a collective activity (something we discuss further in Chapters 9 and 10). Creating a collaborative culture starts with an emphasis on the importance of a collective approach to improving learning for all pupils.

Mathematics subject knowledge

If you are a maths teacher, you will have the qualifications necessary to get started. Knowledge of mathematics is clearly essential, but subject knowledge (as you will see throughout this book) is not a 'have/do not have' dichotomy. Instead, everything on the school curriculum can be understood to a greater or lesser degree of depth and no one, not even a teacher of 40 years, has nothing more to learn or no more connections to make. Whatever your circumstances, it is essential to make sure your knowledge is robust and that you are always learning yourself. When you are preparing to teach something, make sure you can not only complete all the procedures and get the questions correct but that you also know *why* a procedure works and *how* it links to related areas of mathematics — and, for a rounded view, look into how that area of mathematics developed historically. If you are not confident in your own subject knowledge, seek advice from colleagues and use textbooks and online resources to develop your understanding.

There is no shame asking for help as there is always more to learn, even about the seemingly simplest ideas.

Mathematics-specific pedagogical knowledge

Teaching mathematics is different from *doing* mathematics. An excellent mathematician does not automatically know how to develop mathematical knowledge in pupils. Initial teacher training, ongoing professional development and, most importantly, the motivation to spend the time researching and developing your pedagogical subject knowledge are essential for a maths teacher. The knowledge of how mathematical learning develops, how concepts are made clear and how pupils get better at mathematics over time are interlinked with, but not the same as, the knowledge of mathematics itself.

Why this? Why now?

Your school's curriculum plans or scheme of work will heavily influence what you do and when. It is important to understand these plans. Why is this topic taught now? Why do pupils need to know this concept at this point in their mathematical journey?

When faced with a topic to teach, ask yourself these questions:

1. What do pupils learn in this topic?

2. What are the pre-requisites that came before this?

3. What comes after this unit? What does it feed into?

An appreciation of the answers to these questions helps you to see that learning is a continuum and that there are no 'standalone' units of work.

Say your department's scheme of work shows you that over the next two weeks you need to teach 'Factors and multiples', to include: understanding of the terms 'factor' and 'multiple'; the concepts of 'highest common factor' (HCF) and 'lowest common multiple' (LCM); and an introduction to prime numbers.

1. *What do pupils learn in this topic?*

The topic begins with an understanding of the terms factor and multiple and extends to recognition of prime numbers. Pupils will find highest common factors and lowest common multiples by listing and will consider questions in various contexts.

2. *What are the pre-requisites that came before this?*

Children are introduced to the concept of multiplication and multiples from Year 1 by counting in groups. This then develops into times tables. They learn about division and connect this with multiplication then derive multiplication facts beyond the times tables. In Year 5 they identify factors and multiples and learn about prime numbers.

3. *What comes after this unit? What does it feed into?*

Pupils will use these ideas whenever factorising, for example when simplifying fractions or ratios, or factorising algebraic expressions. They will learn about prime factorisation and how to use this to find the HCF and LCM, and other properties of natural numbers.

Planning our mathematical story

Our brains are psychologically predisposed to prioritise stories. We remember them much more easily than information that lacks narrative. The idea of designing a curriculum and sequences of learning to tell a story gives us a framework for our decisions. If we are choosing between several options in the order we teach something, the tasks we use or the methods we demonstrate, having an idea of the narrative we want to gradually reveal helps us to make those decisions.

Leslie Dietiker of Boston University describes the metaphor of 'story' for planning sequences of learning in a paper in which the aspects of story – characters, plot, actions, tension etc. – are used to think about what happens in the mathematics classroom.

Dietiker (2015) tells us that when we sequence mathematical events, they are experienced by the 'reader' as a mathematical story. In our mathematical story, the characters could be numbers, algebraic terms, shapes and so on. The mathematical action is the activity of the 'actor': the pupil, the teacher or a third party described in a word problem. The setting of the story is where the mathematical events happen and could be any representation, model, or manipulative such as a ratio table, Cartesian graph or algebra tiles. The story must have a plot that brings the pupils from what they already know to the new knowledge, sometimes with tension, sometimes with anticipation, and sometimes with a twist. Storytelling works as a metaphor for curriculum, a learning sequence within that curriculum and a lesson within that sequence (we explore this more in Chapter 9).

If, for instance, we want our pupils to learn about prime numbers, then how to decompose a composite number into a product of its prime factors, before applying this prime factorisation in various contexts, we might tell a story a bit like this over a sequence of lessons.

1. All positive integers (natural numbers) have factors.

   ○ Some, like 24, have lots of factors.
   ○ Most have factors in pairs.
   ○ Some have an odd number of factors. These are the square numbers.
   ○ The number 1 is a very special number, the only one that is a factor of all natural numbers.
   ○ Some natural numbers have only two factors. These are special because the two factors are always themselves and 1. We call these prime numbers.
   ○ There is only one even prime number. All the rest are odd.

2. We can multiply prime numbers together to make other numbers. We will call this, 'composing' prime numbers.

   ○ Composing 2 and 3 gives 6. Composing 2, 3 and 5 gives 30. Let's explore which numbers we can make by composing primes.

3. Some natural numbers can't be made by composing primes. These are the prime numbers.

4. Every natural number (greater than 1, because 1 is special) is prime or can be composed from primes.

5. We can take any natural number that is not prime and decompose it. We call this its 'prime factorisation'.

6. We can use this prime factorisation to discover all sorts of things about natural numbers.

   ○ The highest common factor of pairs of numbers.
   ○ The lowest common multiple of pairs of numbers.
   ○ Whether they are square/cube/…
   ○ The number of trailing zeros they have.
   ○ …

The sequence here is a plot summary. It doesn't begin to delve into *how* we tell the story – the questions we ask, the tasks pupils engage in, the problems we set, the solutions we explain, what we make explicit, what we ask them to think about for themselves. These are the considerations that make the story come alive. These are the things that a teacher does to make learning memorable, to help pupils become successful. These are the things that we cover throughout the rest of this book. For now, let's look at some of the major considerations for planning learning.

Planning with questions

A helpful way to begin planning a sequence of learning is to think about the questions that you would like your pupils to be able to answer both throughout the sequence and by the end of it. In our 'Factors and multiples' example, these might include:

Find the highest common factor of each of the following:
a) 56 and 70   b) 24 and 90   c) 90, 135 and 255

We can ask for the lowest common multiple, but it doesn't make sense to ask for the highest common multiple. Explain why this statement is true.

Determine whether these numbers are composite or prime.
a) 147   b) 119   c) 101

Once we have focused our attention on what we want pupils to be able to answer, we can think about the procedures they will need to learn to be able to do this, the concepts they need to develop their understanding, and the tasks we will use to direct their attention to the right things along the way.

Planning to avoid or reduce misconceptions

When learning a concept, pupils will go through stages of poorly formed conceptions and/or even misconceptions, and this is normal in conceptual development. Most misconceptions are understandable and often caused by making an erroneous connection to something already learnt. For example:

'0.35 is greater than 0.5 because 35 is greater than 5.'

In our storytelling metaphor these seemingly logical but erroneous connections can be seen as *conflict*. They give us the opportunity to surprise and challenge pupils and explore with discussion and counterexamples. Make a list of the misconceptions you anticipate will arise when you are planning and discuss them with colleagues, sharing ideas on how to pre-empt or correct them. If we anticipate where the pupils could go wrong, we can plan our explanations and activities accordingly.

We also need to plan *how* we will find out if pupils have developed misconceptions during a learning sequence (this is covered in Chapter 3). While you are teaching, listen carefully to pupils' answers. Often a wrong answer arises because of a misconception, and you will always find times when you did not pre-empt something. Whenever someone gives you a wrong answer, try and figure out where it might have come from (and ask them to explain more if you need to), so that you can fix any underlying misunderstanding or erroneous connection that gave rise to it.

Tasks

> *'There is no other decision that teachers make that has a greater impact on pupils' opportunity to learn and on their perceptions about what mathematics is than the selection or creation of the tasks with which the teacher engages the pupils in studying mathematics.'* (Lappan and Briars, 1995, p. 138)

Once the content and the sequencing of a unit has been decided, we need to think about the tasks pupils will engage with. Tasks should be assessed for value in two main ways: what the pupils will be doing and what they will be thinking about. Cognitive psychologist Daniel Willingham (2021, p. 61) tells us that *'memory is the residue of thought'* and compels us to analyse every lesson in terms of what the pupils will be thinking about. This perspective ensures the planning process isn't *'How can I keep the pupils busy?'* but rather '*How can I make the pupils think hard about the mathematics I want them to learn?'* Which tasks will elicit the most thinking, at the right level of difficulty, on the particular aspect of mathematics that you want the pupils to learn and remember? People think about what they are paying attention to: where will pupils' attention be?

In their book *Mathematical Tasks: The bridge between teaching and learning*, Chris McGrane and Mark McCourt collected the thoughts of teachers and researchers on the tasks that they design and use. The book describes the different types of tasks that can be used in a learning sequence and categorises them in areas such as 'procedural fluency', 'conceptual understanding' and 'problem-solving'. This framework for classification of tasks is helpful to us in focusing our attention on the learning we want to develop in our pupils and how to make that possible through task selection.

If you want pupils to develop procedural fluency, use a task that allows them to practise the procedure repeatedly. Ensure that pupils are always required to think about what they are doing by making the questions they work on increasingly complex or exposing them to different aspects of the procedure that can be difficult. (If pupils can mindlessly churn out correctly answered questions whilst having a chat, then they aren't thinking hard and won't be learning much.) For instance, when adding decimals using whichever algorithm you wish pupils to practise, you will want a variety of numbers with different numbers of digits and with 0 in different places, to ensure they use their knowledge of place value correctly.

Conceptual understanding tasks are designed to help pupils understand the concept underlying a procedure, to reason around what they are learning and to make or strengthen connections between areas of mathematics. These kinds of tasks are essential for developing a robust schema. Without these tasks, mathematics can be reduced to memorisation of processes without discernment of why or when to use them. If conceptual understanding is developed alongside procedural fluency, then the underlying mathematical structures are more likely to be revealed and pupils are more likely to be able to apply their learning in various contexts. The types of activity that help us to teach concepts include:

- using multiple representations;

- sorting mathematical statements (such as the '*always, sometimes, never*' tasks first written by Malcolm Swan in 2005);

- questions that combine 'different' areas of mathematics;

- discussion that helps us to explain our reasoning.

A problem-solving task supports pupils to think and behave mathematically, using their procedural and conceptual knowledge of mathematics. We explore these in more detail in Chapter 5.

In order to compare task types directly, here are examples of tasks from each category, based around the concept of 'highest common factor'.

Procedural	Find the highest common factor of the following: a) 28 and 42 b) 56 and 70 c) 15, 60 and 75 d) 77, 91 and 143
Conceptual	The highest common factor of 24 and 30 is 6. How does this help you find the highest common factor of the following? a) 12 and 15 b) 48 and 60 c) 36 and 45 d) 24 and 15
Problem-Solving	Jenny has 3 pieces of ribbon with lengths of 140 cm, 168 cm and 210 cm. She needs to cut all of them so that they are equal in length with no leftover ribbon. What is the longest possible length of each of the smaller pieces of ribbon? How many smaller pieces of ribbon does Jenny get altogether?

Participation and thinking

At every point in a learning sequence, we need to consider our pupils' means of participation. Are they working independently in silence? Are they working with a partner, discussing what they are doing? Are they using mini-whiteboards so you can check for understanding? Are they recording their work in their books? There is a place for all types of participation, but you should organise activities so that participation is always maximised. Don't be afraid to make independent work genuinely independent and silent: this is important for allowing pupils time and space to get their heads round the work. Don't be afraid to have periods of discussion, allowing pupils to vocalise their thoughts and bounce ideas off each other, so long as these are managed well to ensure pupils' attention remains on the task at hand. Don't worry if not everything is written down in their books – that doesn't mean they haven't been thinking hard. Similarly, don't avoid asking pupils to practise writing mathematics in a clear and precise way. Part of learning mathematics is learning to communicate it in spoken *and* written form.

We mentioned above that tasks should be set at the 'right level' of difficulty. The right level is a troublesome thing to gauge. It is that which pushes pupils to learn more than they already know without it being beyond them. We want activity and tasks that are not so easy the pupils get bored and not so difficult that they give up. A bit like when you do a good puzzle, game or quiz – one that makes you think but with some prospect of success. The difficulty in selecting the level of the task is that all classes are in some way 'mixed ability', even if you have setting in your school. All pupils have had different experiences which bring them to the point that they engage in the task, and they will approach it from their own unique combination of those experiences. The best tasks allow all pupils access, maybe with some scaffolding or prompting, but also allow pupils to deepen their understanding through some productive struggle.

When selecting a task, consider the aspect of the concept or procedure you would like the pupils to think about. It is tempting to come across an interesting, entertaining activity and think, 'That's a nice task, the pupils will love it (and I will feel like a successful teacher)', then fit the teaching around it. There is merit in planning enjoyable tasks that will hold the attention of the pupils – remember, we want their attention – but we must ensure the nature of a task is subservient to the *mathematics* that we are teaching. The relationship of the task to the planned mathematical content is the most important reason it should be selected.

Sometimes a task could be enjoyable but does not contribute to the narrative or story we are telling through our learning sequences and through our curriculum. The short-term gain of 'I enjoyed that' should not outweigh the use of carefully selected tasks that move pupils further along their path of knowledge and understanding.

It is also useful to consider that any task is, in itself, insufficient to maximise learning. How it is used in the classroom can make or break it. Imagine you want your pupils to explore the link between multiples and prime numbers in more depth, and you choose to use the Sieve of Eratosthenes. The Sieve is an important demonstration of primes, it shows the links between different multiples, and working with a hundred square reveals interesting patterns. The Sieve does indeed reveal the prime numbers, but how it is used in the classroom can present a challenge: what are the pupils thinking about and concentrating on when they complete this activity?

Let's consider one way of using the Sieve in the classroom. A printed hundred square is given to each pupil along with some coloured pencils. Instructions are written on the board:

Colour in the multiples of 2, except 2 itself.
Colour in the multiples of 3, except 3 itself.
Colour in the multiples of 5, except 5 itself.
Continue to go to the next blank square. Leave it blank but colour in all its multiples.
Well done, you have discovered the prime numbers!

Let's look at what the pupils are attending to here. They may be thinking about what colours they will use, then what the multiples of 2 are, very quickly going through the grid colouring in every other number. They might be concerned with staying in the lines as they colour. They will then colour the other multiples as directed, potentially without much more thought than 'every third number', and so on. The majority of pupils in secondary school can do this task with minimal thought while chatting to a friend. By the end, the pupils have thought about the positioning of multiples on a hundred square and about colouring. As it is, this task is not optimal for thinking about prime numbers. It is missing thinking about factors; there is no explicit contrasting of primes with composite numbers to expose why the primes are unique. If left there, pupils' understanding of primes will be sorely lacking. At best, they will appreciate that the primes are not in any of the 'times tables'. At worst, it occupies them with colouring in until they have a pretty list of prime numbers to stick in their book.

1	2	3	4	5	6	7	8	9	10
11	12	13	14	15	16	17	18	19	20
21	22	23	24	25	26	27	28	29	30
31	32	33	34	35	36	37	38	39	40
41	42	43	44	45	46	47	48	49	50
51	52	53	54	55	56	57	58	59	60
61	62	63	64	65	66	67	68	69	70
71	72	73	74	75	76	77	78	79	80
81	82	83	84	85	86	87	88	89	90
91	92	93	94	95	96	97	98	99	100

Does this mean we abandon the Sieve? Not at all. There are better ways to approach the same activity.

On the excellent NRICH website (https://nrich.maths. org/7520/note), different possible approaches are outlined with structured questioning to guide the pupils' thinking. This encourages them to predict what might happen before they set out on a set of multiples, to explain why they sometimes colour in a square already coloured, and to imagine which numbers would be crossed out last on grids of different sizes. It also asks pupils how they can be sure. It ends with the question, *'Which possible factors do we need to consider in order to decide if a number is prime?'* While this version of the activity does not reveal all the ways of thinking about prime numbers (no single task could), it increases the chance that the pupils are thinking mathematically about the concepts involved.

Another version of the Sieve uses a number grid with only six columns. Numbers are shaded as per the original instructions but there is an extra interesting piece of information to be noticed from it.

Take a look at the example below. What do you notice about the prime numbers? Can you justify to yourself that this is always true?

1	2	3	4	5	6
7	8	9	10	11	12
13	14	15	16	17	18
19	20	21	22	23	24
25	26	27	28	29	30
31	32	33	34	35	36
37	38	39	40	41	42
43	44	45	46	47	48
49	50	51	52	53	54
55	56	57	58	59	60
61	62	63	64	65	66
67	68	69	70	71	72

Our example highlights the importance of instructional design and of implementing tasks in a way that makes pupils think hard about the mathematics. If the planning process is reduced to merely selecting tasks or worksheets, and no thought is given to how that task will be delivered to optimise learning, then the purpose and/or benefits of it can be lost. Put simply, you need to consider what you will be doing and saying, and what the pupils will be doing and (hopefully) thinking about, during any task you choose to use. In our storytelling metaphor this can be thought of as the prose of the learning sequence; how the story progresses from what the pupils know at the beginning of the topic to where they will be at the end.

Representations and methods

Representations are the symbols, models, and manipulatives that we use to communicate mathematically. We describe many of these in more detail in Chapter 4.

To help us think about what constitutes a representation, below is a collection of representations of the concept 'quadratic function', each revealing a different aspect of the concept.

When planning a sequence of learning, you should think carefully about the representations you use. Pupils make sense of the abstract nature of mathematics through representation, and they form part of a pupil's understanding that each subsequent learning sequence and teacher should build on. Working collaboratively with the other teachers in your department to come to a consensus on how to teach a topic, including the representations you will use, will lead to deep discussions about which models reveal the aspect of the mathematics that you want the pupils to think about. Shared approaches are a good way of ensuring consistency of a pupil's

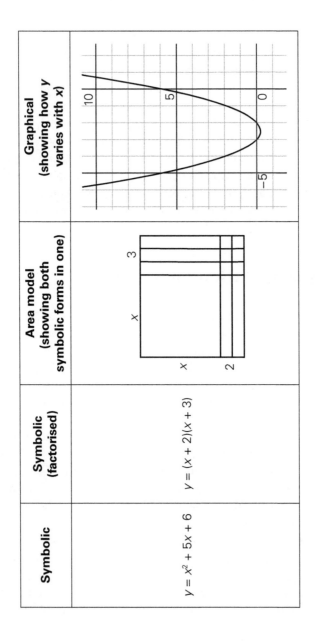

Symbolic	Symbolic (factorised)	Area model (showing both symbolic forms in one)	Graphical (showing how y varies with x)
$y = x^2 + 5x + 6$	$y = (x + 2)(x + 3)$		

learning experience, whoever teaches them. Collaborative planning brings together the wealth of experience that will exist in the department and encourages us to take the time to think more deeply and develop our mathematics-specific pedagogical knowledge. We can consider each representation as a thread woven through the curriculum, a setting for the story we are telling (more on this in Chapter 9).

This gives us an imperative for building consistency of representations and methods within a department. This is not always the case in schools, where teachers can often select representations and methods based on what they prefer, sometimes because they were taught that way, or sometimes because a particular representation or method fits with the teacher's own understanding and conceptual knowledge.

For example, there are many, many ways of presenting the process of 'expanding two brackets'. Over the years, we have seen the following:

1. The 'smiley face'

$(x + 3)(x + 2)$

2. 'FOIL' (first, outers, inners, last)

$(x + 3)(x + 2)$

F x^2
O $2x$
I $3x$
L 6

3. The 'crab's claw' or 'parrot's beak'

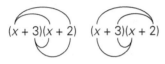

$(x + 3)(x + 2)$ $(x + 3)(x + 2)$

4. Grid multiplication and area model

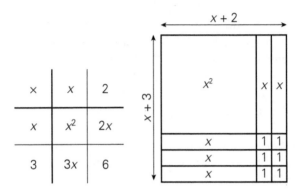

×	x	2
x	x^2	$2x$
3	$3x$	6

5. Inline multiplication

$$(x + 3)(x + 2) = x(x + 2) + 3(x + 2)$$
$$= x^2 + 2x + 3x + 6$$
$$= x^2 + 5x + 6$$

As a teacher, you know that these are all slightly different ways of presenting the exact same process. A pupil who is still getting to grips with things will not. If this pupil goes from one class to another and different presentations are used, they will have to try to make sense of something new before they can access what the teacher is showing them. This places an unnecessary obstacle in the pupil's way.

In his book *Teaching Mathematics at Secondary Level*, Tony Gardiner advises us to: 'routinely re-visit old material and replace old methods by more flexible, forward-looking alternatives. Distinguish clearly between backward-looking methods (that may deliver answers, but which hinder progression) and forward-looking methods (that may at first seem unnecessarily difficult, but which hold the key to future progression)' Every method or representation of a process should be analysed in light of this.

Some of the examples above, for expanding two brackets, could be seen as backward-looking, only 'working' as a one-off in a specific context while also obscuring some of the underlying structure of the mathematics. For instance, it is not obvious why all the terms should be added together in the first three examples in our list above. That we must multiply along the arcs and add is something that pupils must just accept. The grid method, if already familiar from numerical multiplication and if linked to an area model, however, makes the need to add more obvious, linking algebraic multiplication explicitly to numerical multiplication. The inline presentation, where each term in the first bracket is multiplied by the whole of the second bracket, before further expanding and simplifying, has the benefit of presenting the mathematics in a clear and well-communicated way, but lacks the visual element that might link it to prior learning.

The grid method and inline presentation are more likely forward-looking, one in terms of building conceptual links, one in terms of building clarity of communication. Take time on your own and with your team to, as Gardiner advises, revisit old material and old ways of working and check that they are flexible, forward-looking, and fit the mathematical story you are trying to tell.

Language

The language we use in the classroom can either actively help pupils to think mathematically or can make it harder for them to do so. We need pupils to have access to subject-specific words and phrases to enable them to participate in mathematical discourse. We tend to think about these 'key words' early in our planning. They are perhaps written on curriculum documents, lesson presentation materials and into pupils' books. When planning learning sequences, we need to think about how we will define them, use them, and enable pupils to remember them.

One way that we can make key words memorable and make sense to pupils is to discuss their etymology. The word 'geometry', for example, means 'measuring the earth'. Ask pupils what other words they know that contain 'geo' (maybe 'geography', 'geode', 'geology' or 'geocaching') or a variant of 'metry' (maybe 'metre', 'perimeter' or 'metric') and discuss how these words are related. When pupils understand the origins of a word, and other words in the etymological family, they can make more sense of it.

In our planning we should think about how we will provide opportunities for pupils to use rigorous mathematical language, argument and reasoning in our classroom interactions. One way we can do this is to model using it ourselves. Then, when a pupil gives an answer, insist that they use the correct mathematical language, rephrasing or redrafting their answer where necessary. For instance, a classroom interaction that focuses on speaking mathematically might look like this:

Teacher: (with $\frac{1}{3} + \frac{7}{9}$ written on the board): *What do we have to do before we can find the sum of these two fractions?*

Pupil: *You just times the top and bottom numbers by the same number and get a fraction that has the same bottom number as the other one.*

Teacher: *I know what you're trying to say, but you can say that more clearly. Look at the words written on the board here.* [Points to the words 'numerator', 'denominator' and 'common denominator' kept on the edge of the board.] *Can you rephrase your answer using them?*

Pupil: *Multiply both the numerator and the denominator of the first fraction by the same number so that there is a common denominator to both fractions.*

By giving the pupil an opportunity to rehearse mathematical language out loud, you are helping them to internalise it.

Language is also used to connect all our mathematical representations – symbolic, pictorial and concrete. Verbal explanations, questions and internal dialogue develop understanding of an abstract concept. Planning your language, explanations and questioning should go hand in hand with planning tasks or selecting the most useful representations. Writing down and rehearsing some key questions or statements associated with each phase of the learning sequence will make it more likely that you use these ideas in the classroom. Think about your language in terms of being forward-looking – never say anything now that could store up problems in the future, such as the classic 'to multiply by 10, add a zero'. This might work today, when pupils are multiplying integers, but will not work in the future when they are multiplying decimals. Nor does it connect with the model you are most likely to have used: the place value table.

Enriching learning

When we think about enriching learning, we usually intend to expose pupils to an experience beyond the essential instruction and tasks that give them the knowledge to meet the scope of the National Curriculum and pass their SATs, GCSEs or A Level exams. One of the ways we can enrich the curriculum is to include knowledge that, while not necessary to complete the task, deepens its significance. We might discuss the contexts in which areas of maths are applied in different jobs. (A word of warning: don't refer to contextual or applied mathematics as 'real-life' mathematics. This phrase risks communicating that the classroom, and the intellectual pursuit of mathematics for its own sake, is not 'real life' and is therefore of lesser importance.) We might look at the history of the mathematics at hand, not just to see how it developed but to 'humanise' it and to stop maths seeming like something that 'just is'. We might deepen our learning of a topic by including related mathematics outside of the scope of the statutory curriculum, such as exploring different number bases when learning about place value. By considering how and where mathematical knowledge evolved, its relevance, and how it fits into a bigger picture we afford pupils more access to the fascinating historical and contemporary importance of our subject. This 'hinterland knowledge' is explored more in Chapter 6. Enrichment should be seen as an integral part of planning, not an add-on left to those who plan clubs and trips.

Homework

Homework, while compulsory in most schools, can be overlooked in planning. Sometimes it is seen as an add-on or a 'fit in with the whole-school policy and set anything because I have to' event. Homework, if required, should be planned carefully, with thought to its purpose and how we communicate that purpose to pupils. The quality of a homework task is more important than the quantity. We could set a task to practise prerequisite knowledge for an upcoming learning sequence, for example, or to interrupt the 'forgetting cycle' or to rehearse something that was covered in class. Homework should never be set as 'busy work' to keep a pupil occupied. It is important that pupils and their parents or carers see its value since it, by definition, takes up precious personal or family time at the evening or weekend. Everyone involved will be more likely to see homework as valuable if you explain its purpose and why you think it will enhance learning. (And follow it up too. A quick call, text or email to parents about a homework success or missing homework can work wonders.)

The Education Endowment Foundation (n.d. (a)) found homework to have a positive effect on learning while pointing out that it is one of the areas that widens the gap of disadvantage. Those who complete it do better; those who don't do worse. In order not to actively widen this gap, we must pay attention to how equitable the homework is, or not.

If a pupil must rely on parents or carers to complete their homework, then this gap will widen. Pupils should be able to access the task themselves and be given clear instructions on what to do and when it should be returned, since confusion will lead to negativity and non-completion. If each homework task you set is different, and pupils have to make sense of them in your absence (after a long day when they were given the instructions hours earlier), you are less likely to have a high success rate. If you always set homework in the same way, such as on an online platform, you reduce the risk that a pupil will not know how to access the work. But if there is nowhere at home to sit quietly to do work or a device to access the technology is required, then the pupil is at further disadvantage. Provide access to a homework club, or the school computer room or library, to support those who cannot complete it successfully at home, and be sure to check that the methods in any videos don't confuse pupils with how you have taught them.

If you set the same work to all pupils, such that it takes one group five minutes and another group one hour, you are unfairly taking away the personal time of those who find mathematics more difficult. This is not equitable. Ensure that your homework is appropriate to the level pupils are working at, that its volume is fair for all (even if this means setting different amounts or types of task to different groups of pupils) and that it genuinely helps them to embed their learning. Support pupils in completing the work and reward them when they do.

Planning from prepared resources

Many departments and multi-academy trusts provide partially or fully resourced curricula for teachers to use. This can be a huge advantage if it is of good quality, as it reduces the workload of finding tasks and activities. It can also mean the curriculum is coherent and follows a clear story. It does, however, come with its own set of pitfalls.

If you are presented with a scheme of learning, guidance notes, lesson presentation materials and some worksheets (or a booklet or textbook) and, at the same time, you feel like the busiest person in the world, it is tempting to deprioritise planning. The truth is that although teaching materials have been prepared, they have not been created by you. They follow someone else's thought processes and someone else's opinions on how to teach. Even the best quality resources like this will fall flat if you do not still prepare the learning sequence thoroughly. It is your responsibility to bring the material to life, to use your mathematics-specific pedagogy to stop a lesson becoming 'click and play'.

Lesson preparation is crucial. Spend time thinking about the sequencing of tasks, about your explanations and questions, about the means of pupil participation, about possible misconceptions, and about what pupils will be thinking about throughout the learning sequence. A well-prepared learning sequence is the backbone of our practice. In the subsequent chapters, we will move onto the rest of the body.

Chapter Summary

In this chapter we have we have explored some ideas that we should consider when planning learning.

- Collaborating with colleagues will deepen pedagogical knowledge, promote consistency, and improve learning.
- Learning should be seen as a continuum rather than a series of disconnected topics.
- Doing maths and teaching maths are connected but not the same. Plan what you will say and how you will explain and represent the maths. Remember that your understanding of the mathematics is not the same as the journey pupils will take to get there.
- Anticipate and plan for misconceptions.
- The selection of the right task at the right time is essential. The task should lead the pupils to think about the relevant maths.

FURTHER READING

Mathematical Tasks: The bridge between teaching and learning Chris McGrane and Mark McCourt (2020) is a brilliant read to help you think more deeply about which tasks to use in the classroom.

Teaching Mathematics at Secondary Level by Tony Gardiner (2016) is a clear explanation of how to make mathematics teaching effective and connected.

Making Every Maths Lesson Count by Emma McCrea (2019) is a handbook on how to craft reliably successful lessons.

2

Some practicalities of classroom instruction

Once we are in the classroom, our role changes from planning *how* pupils will make sense of mathematics to creating an environment that *enables* them to do so. Every action we take can have an effect on what is learnt and how well it is learnt. In this chapter, we will explore some of the many practices and ideas that make up classroom instruction. Some of the things you might expect to see here have chapters of their own, and this chapter is not exhaustive (nothing ever could be!) but we hope it gives you plenty of food for thought.

In Chapter 1 we looked at the idea of learning sequences – blocks in which we use activities and tasks to help pupils move from no or limited knowledge of an idea to more or deeper knowledge. These sequences may take ten minutes or they may take ten days. Some of the ideas in this chapter may not take place in every learning sequence and it is important never to be too prescriptive with what you expect to see in any one lesson. Every pupil and teacher activity, every teacher action, must be in service to the mathematics that is to be taught and not the other way around.

Exemplification

Part of the process of learning mathematics is seeing processes and procedures exemplified, mimicking procedures and practising until we know how to do them. Worked examples are very common in mathematics classrooms; often they're the main means by which we demonstrate procedures to our pupils. A well-crafted worked example communicates a process clearly, without distracting features, and helps pupils to make sense of the mathematics underlying a procedure. However, not every worked example is created equal. It is possible to enhance their use and it is possible to use them badly. One of our first considerations when picking examples should be how well they help us to communicate the mathematics.

Consider the example:

$$1 + x = 7$$

The constants and coefficients in this example are limited to small, easy-to-manipulate integers, so most pupils can solve this by sight or by means of substitution. While this should not be discouraged, if the intention is to teach pupils how to solve equations by rearrangement, then this example may distract the pupils from that purpose, as it does not demonstrate the need of practising rearrangement. Some may switch off from instruction thinking they can 'already do it'. In order to be effective, this example would need to be an initial part of a group of more complex examples. The next one, for instance, could be one that cannot be easily solved by sight, in order to show pupils that they need better strategies.

$$167 + x = 1982$$

This brings something else for us to consider. We don't want arithmetic to get in the way of success for our pupils. This question may cause a distraction for some, with the focus now being on arithmetic. If you know some pupils are not fluent with arithmetic yet, consider giving them a calculator so their attention remains on solving equations by rearrangement.

Representations (symbols, imagery and concrete manipulatives) form an essential part of exemplification. A process without any kind of understanding reduces mathematics to an exercise of memory, giving an unfair advantage to those who have stronger recall. We should always consider which representations we can use to best communicate the mathematics in our worked examples. Consider the addition rule for probability:

$$P(A \cup B) = P(A) + P(B) - P(A \cap B)$$

A purely written approach might involve substituting in probabilities and rearranging this formula. But without imagery, it can be hard to interpret this formula and 'see' what is going on. The structure of the mathematics is better revealed by exploring other representations alongside this formula. One way we can communicate its structure is through a two-way table.

	Has a sister	Does not have a sister	Total
Has a brother	43	62	105
Does not have a brother	72	12	84
Total	115	74	189

To find the number of people who have a sister or a brother ($S \cup B$), we might start by adding the number of those who have a brother (105) to those who have a sister (115). By drawing imagery such as a Venn diagram, we see that the intersection – those who have a sister *and* a brother – is repeated in this addition, so we must subtract 43 to reach the correct answer. Compare this process with the formula above and the formula comes to life.

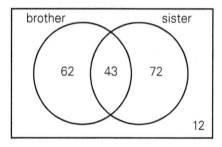

Each representation has its pros and cons. In this example, the table shows all the possibilities more clearly, but can become number overload. The Venn diagram reveals the formula more easily as it has fewer numbers to consider but is more obscure when thinking about totals. It is good to show different representations, but we need to consider when to do this. When we are introducing a new concept to novice learners, we need to be conscious of where their focus will be and whether the imagery may cause any faulty thinking. Too much, too soon, and there's a risk we will overload them. This is something we get better at with practice and reflection, as is generally the case with most of teaching.

Attention

When teaching, we must always keep the key concept we are teaching at the front of our minds. It is very easy to get distracted from this and, mistakenly, draw pupils' attention to the wrong things. Imagine a lesson where the teacher is teaching distance–time graphs, and specifically the fact that the gradient of the graph represents the speed of travel. There is a graph on the board like this:

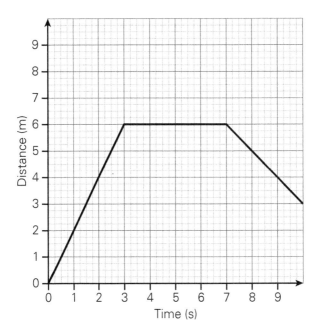

The teacher explains to the pupils that to calculate the speed for the first part of the journey, they must find the gradient of the first line segment. They write $\frac{6}{3} =$ on the board and then ask the class, *'And what is 6 divided by 3?'* The pupils respond with 2, because they know how to divide, and the teacher responds with a general *'Well done'*, thinking that the class understands how to find the speed, and sets them off on independent practice. Lots of pupils get stuck quite quickly, even though they seemed to be successful minutes before. The key to discerning what has happened here is to look at the pupils' attention in the period of instruction. Questions direct pupils' attention very well. In this period of instruction, the only question was one of (easy, for this class) mental arithmetic. The pupils were not tested on their understanding of how to find gradient, or of the fact that the gradient represents the speed, only on whether they could find $\frac{6}{3}$. As a result, their attention was drawn towards mental arithmetic and away from the key concepts of the lesson.

Whenever you ask questions in a lesson, use them to draw the attention of as many pupils as possible to the key concepts you want them to learn. Pupils are more likely to learn what they focus on.

Example-problem pairs

Introduced by Craig Barton in his book *How I Wish I'd Taught Maths* (2018), example-problem pairs are now very common in English schools. Barton draws on the work of cognitive scientist John Sweller who explored the 'worked example effect,' which suggests that studying worked examples prepares pupils to solve problems independently. The idea of an example-problem pair is that pupils see a clear exposition from the teacher and immediately get the chance to replicate the process themselves.

One clear way to do this is to split the board into two columns: 'My Turn' and 'Your Turn'. During the 'My Turn,' pupils silently watch the teacher model and explain. The focus is on giving a clear exposition with minimal interruption. The 'Your Turn' is not revealed until the teacher is ready for pupils to try for themselves, so that pupils are not tempted to stop listening and have a go, potentially missing something important. Here is an example of an example-problem pair.

Prime factor decomposition	
My turn	Your turn
Write these numbers as a product of prime factors.	Write these numbers as a product of prime factors.
a. 15	a. 35
b. 20	b. 45

In the 'My turn' above, 15 is carefully selected – it is the product of two prime numbers so only one step is required. The second, 20, is slightly more difficult; there is more than one factor pair we can choose initially. We might want to highlight that all starting points reach the same decomposition. (Or we might want to leave that until later. The decision depends on knowing what is best for each group of pupils.) On the right, there are mathematically similar examples for pupils to try themselves immediately after the example has been modelled. The use of mini-whiteboards as a means of checking for understanding here can be very powerful and there is more on this in Chapter 3.

Explaining and questioning

At this point, we should pause and consider what constitutes a 'clear exposition'. When we think about our exposition, we should think about:

- precise mathematical language;
- easy-to-follow sentences (without waffle);
- potential use of imagery as well as symbols or text;

- clear presentation on the board;
- judicious use of colour to help draw attention to the most important aspects.

Questioning should be considered separately to explaining. The two are related and can overlap, but they are not interchangeable.

To explain this a little more, we should point out that it is not uncommon for teachers to try to explain things through questions. '*Who can think what the first step might be?*,' '*What should I do next?*,' '*How can I check if this is correct?*' and so on. The problem with a guess-what's-in-my-head approach is that those pupils who can figure it out will do so, but those who cannot have not benefited from a clear exposition and will feel like they do not understand. Instead, they have tried to make sense of the (potentially incomplete or poorly explained) ideas of their peers, interrupted by prompts from the teacher. It is important that those who need explanations are given them. The understanding of all pupils (even those who might be able to figure it out for themselves) will be much greater if they have seen an exposition of high quality followed by the chance to practise for themselves. When we take questioning out of our initial exposition we can focus on its clarity and quality and make much better use of our questions at other times to probe pupils' thinking more deeply, to make them think about unexpected aspects of a concept, or to challenge their misconceptions.

Questions draw a person's attention to something. In a lesson, when our time is limited, we should use our questions to check for pupils' understanding (see Chapter 3) and to direct pupils' attention to important or interesting aspects once they are getting to grips with the maths. To illustrate the point further, consider which of these (real-life) episodes in a lesson is likely to result in greater success for all.

Version 1	Version 2
The teacher wants to use a worked example of finding the lowest common multiple. They start by asking, *'Who thinks they know what "lowest common multiple" means?'* and gets a few ideas, none of which is correct. They then show on the board the question, *'What is the lowest common multiple of 6 and 9?'* The teacher asks the pupils what the multiples of 6 and 9 are, and they start to list them, getting pupils to tell her the next and the next. They then ask the question on the board. One pupil figures it out and volunteers their answer. The teacher says, *'Well done!'* then gets everyone to try a similar question on their mini-whiteboards. Lots of pupils are not sure what to do so the teacher goes through another example, again asking questions. Fifteen minutes into the episode, the pupils start working on some independent practice.	The teacher wants to use a worked example of finding the lowest common multiple. They start with the question, *'What is the lowest common multiple of 6 and 9?'* then lists the first 12 multiples of each number. They ask pupils to write on their mini-whiteboards which multiples are common to each list, checking that all the pupils can make sense of the idea of 'common multiples' by writing down 18 and 36. They then ask them to circle the lowest of the two. *'This,'* the teacher tells pupils, *'is the lowest common multiple of 6 and 9.'* The teacher writes on the board, *'$LCM(6,9) = 18$',* then provides pupils with a similar question to complete on their mini-whiteboards. They are happy that they have the gist of the concept, so they set them off on some independent practice. The whole episode lasts ten minutes.

In Version 1, some pupils expressed a correct notion of multiples in the initial discussion but no one knew what the lowest common multiple was. The remainder of the class heard these poorly formed responses as part of their first encounter with the phrase 'lowest common multiple,' instead of the teacher's carefully crafted exposition. This led to confusion and time-wasting and it is these sorts of interactions that can be responsible for pupils forming partial conceptions of an idea or developing misconceptions. This approach can also turn periods of instruction into periods of endless interrogation, which are not conducive to focus.

Version 2 took less time and afforded every pupil a clear explanation, along with a check for understanding. This episode is more likely to lead to greater success for all pupils and, importantly, frees up time and space for questioning to be more provoking later on.

It seems that sometimes we can be afraid to tell our pupils how to do something, perhaps under a misguided notion that they must discover things for themselves or that we mustn't talk at them too much. In Version 1 above, the process of questioning did not help pupils to discover for themselves; rather it left too many of them confused. Remember, you are the expert in the classroom, and it is a good thing to tell your pupils exactly how to do something. Combine this with thought-provoking questioning at the right times to make them think deeply and their mathematical knowledge and understanding will be greater.

In the context of our learning episode on lowest common multiples, the kinds of questions that will provoke deeper thought once pupils have grasped the basic concept might include, *'Is it possible to have a highest common multiple?'* or *'How many pairs of numbers can you find whose LCM is 24?'* as well as contextual questions where the phrase 'lowest common multiple' is not explicit, or those that compare and contrast the concept with that of highest common factor.

Standard and non-standard examples

Below are two series of questions on the topic of 'expanding two brackets'. Take a moment to look through the two series and consider the differences between the two.

Standard examples	Non-standard examples
$(x+4)(x+3)$	$(4+x)(x+3)$
$(x-7)(x+2)$	$(x-7)(2+x)$
$(x+1)(x-5)$	$(x+1+y)(x-5)$
$(x-2)(x-3)$	$(3-x)(2-x)$
$(2x+7)(x+3)$	$(2x+y)(x+z)$

Those on the left are the kind used most often in classrooms. Once a pupil has got to grips with the process of expansion using questions like these, they may have certain assumptions about bracketed expressions of this form – perhaps they will implicitly think that the x term has to be at the front of each bracket, or always has to be positive. It is important that they see examples like those on the right to challenge any erroneous assumptions. The expressions $(4+x)(x+3)$ and $(x-7)(2+x)$ show that x can go anywhere, while $(3-x)(2-x)$ shows it can be negative within the brackets. The example $(x+1+y)(x-5)$ highlights that a bracket can contain more than two terms and $(2x+y)(x+z)$ shows that we can use any combination of letters. Through practice with non-standard examples, pupils' understanding of a concept or process is strengthened.

Using mistakes

Mistakes can sometimes be a natural slip-up, but often they tell us what pupils need to learn. In his book, *Teaching Math with Examples* (2021), Michael Pershan advocates using pupils' mistakes as an inspiration for worked examples, drawing on the work of McGinn, Lange and Booth who suggest we start the design of our examples by considering pupils' common mistakes and targeting worked examples to one error or misconception at a time. Luckily, we have access to pupil mistakes at our fingertips. *Diagnostic Questions* (www.diagnosticquestions.com) is one of the fantastic websites created by Craig Barton, where teachers can freely access well-designed multiple-choice questions and invaluable pupil data from across the world – giving every teacher the insight of pupils' mistakes that crop up repeatedly.

Diagnostic Questions includes an insights tab, where you can see the most common misconception. For instance, adding the indices is a very common misconception for a question like this.

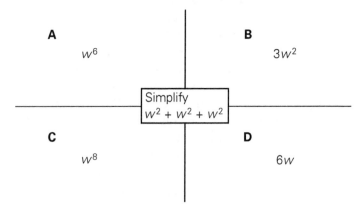

The incorrect answers are not random. They include 'distractors' and are carefully designed to diagnose misconceptions. Answer A reveals the misconception where pupils confuse the calculation with multiplying the terms, applying the laws of indices and adding the exponents. C is where pupils think they need to multiply the exponents because they are multiplying the terms. Answer D conflates w^2 with $2w$.

Often pupils learn about adding expressions before multiplying them, but topics learnt later can cause confusion with those that were taught earlier. When teaching the multiplication of expressions, after pupils have shown good understanding, it is vital that we use worked examples to prevent pupils confusing the two operations in their newly formed schema.

This could be done by placing $w^4 \times w^4 = w^8$ next to $w^4 + w^4 = 2w^4$ and asking pupils, *'What is the same; what is different?'* and giving them practice exercises where they have to identify the correct solution to a series of questions that mix addition and multiplication of expressions. These 'method selection' activities are important to help pupils distinguish between readily confused procedures. If we use method selection too early in the sequence of learning, before pupils have grasped the multiplication of terms, we are in danger of overloading their working memories (more on this in Chapter 7) or feed into misconceptions. Große and Renkl (2004, p. 363) say that *'in early stages of the learning process only correct solutions should be provided, whereas in later stages the presentation of incorrect examples can be effective'.*

Pershan agrees with this, telling us that *'in general, mistake analysis works only when pupils have some experience solving the problem correctly'.* He draws on the work of the SERP Institute's *Algebra by Example* project (www.serpinstitute.org/algebra-by-example), where examples are clearly marked as incorrect and include self-explanation prompts for pupils. The main benefits come from explaining why a wrong idea is incorrect; not from discovering the error.

Chris tried to simplify this expression but didn't do it correctly. Here is his working:

$2(3 - 7x) - 4(x - 2)$

$6 - 14x - 4x - 8$

$-2 - 18x$

- Why is the −8 incorrect?

- If Chris had expanded his brackets correctly, what should he have gotten as an answer in simplest form?

Your turn:

$3(2 - 7x) - 4(2 - x)$

The numbers you use matter

Let us consider the introduction of square numbers. It seems logical to start with examples in numerical order: with 1^2, then 2^2, and so on. The squares of 1 and 2 can 'feel' different to the other squares, by virtue of the fact that 1^2 is 1 – this doesn't happen for any other square number – and 2^2 is 4, which is also the double of 2 – something that, again, doesn't happen for any other square number (apart from 0^2, of course, but that's another special case). Instead of starting with these examples, which could be described as a little quirky, we could start with 3^2 and 4^2 and so on before coming back to 1^2 and 2^2, highlighting their quirkiness in the process. The advantage of this is that once pupils are happy with the idea of squaring, we can then draw their attention to the one people most often slip up on (anyone teaching for a long time has heard plenty of pupils say that 1^2 is 2), and we may be less likely to induce the misconception that squaring is doubling which the sight of $2^2 = 4$ could encourage.

Sometimes correct answers can be found in incorrect ways. This is something we want to avoid in initial instruction. Consider this question below:

The table shows information about the number of pets 300 students have.

Number of pets	Frequency
0	3
1	57
2	84
3	75
4	81

Find the median number of pets.

The correct answer is 3 but the following incorrect solutions would get you there.

- Calculate the mean to the nearest integer and the answer is 3. $774 \div 300 = 2.58 \approx 3$ to 1 s.f.

- Order the frequencies – 3, 57, 75, 81, 84 – and find the middle value, which is 75. This frequency is for 3 pets.

Before using a question as an example in the classroom, check that the answer cannot be obtained through incorrect means, as you might find it hard to assess pupils' understanding. There are some more questions below where incorrect working gets the 'correct' answer.

Write the fraction $\dfrac{16}{64}$ in its simplest form If pupils cross out the 6 in the numerator and denominator, they will obtain the correct answer of $\dfrac{1}{4}$.	Simplify $a^2 \times a^2$ If pupils multiply the indices, they will get the correct simplification of a^4.
Work out the value of x 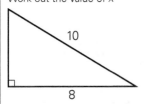 If pupils follow an apparent pattern of subtracting two to the length each time, they will get the correct length of 6 cm through the wrong means. (This can be the case for any 3-4-5 similar triangle).	Find the nth term of the sequence: 6, 9, 12, 15, 18, … The 3 is repeated in the nth term $3n + 3$ as the coefficient of n and the constant. Pupils will struggle to see how the different parts of the nth term relate to the features of the sequence if they are the same numbers.

What you say matters

In the introduction we talked about habits – how we form positive and negative ones through daily repetition and how the way to break negative habits, or to create new positive ones, is to be a reflective practitioner and to actively rehearse the behaviours we want to embed. Part of this process of reflection involves thinking carefully about what you say and how you say it, both mathematically and more generally.

We can all get nervous or distracted in the classroom. It might be the first time you have taught a topic, there might be an external visitor in your classroom, or it might be snowing outside. Whatever the reason, we can waffle, unnecessarily repeat things, forget crucial parts of our exposition, and add redundant information or filler words. Filler words are those such as, *'Okay!'*, '*Okay?'* (both different!), *'Sorry'* or *'Right!'* They clutter what you are saying, can make it hard for pupils to follow you, and they often stem from seeking approval from the pupils. If you show signs of doubting yourself, your pupils might start to doubt you too. This can lead to difficulties in trust and relationships, which are hard to rebuild. Redundant phrases are those that offer nothing of value and include things like, *'This bit's obvious/easy/basic,'* or '*You don't really need to know this, but…'* or *'They won't ask you this in an exam.'* There is never a time where declaring that something is obvious or easy will be helpful for the pupils in your classroom. Those that are struggling to grasp the idea will be more likely to feel that cannot seek your help or support if you say things like this and they may begin to feel like they are not good at mathematics. In a similar way, communicating somehow that something you are doing is not important (because it's not on an exam or because it's outside the curriculum) is a sure-fire way to indirectly tell pupils they can switch off.

One way to combat redundancy in your speech is to script your teacher exposition beforehand. This can be done independently or with a colleague. Without the hindrance of classroom distractions and pressures, this allows you to focus on:

- Your choice of key words and vocabulary – *are you explaining a new concept with words that your pupils understand already?*

- Connecting new content with previous knowledge – *are you making these connections explicit to the pupils?*

- Streamlining your communication – *are you saying things as clearly and as concisely as possible, removing any redundant information or filler words?*

- The parts you are going to draw your pupils' attention to – *which knowledge matters?*

- The best way to communicate the mathematics - *is there a possibility your explanation may cause future faulty thinking?*

Misconceptions are abundant in mathematics, so we must reduce the chance that they are caused from the explanations and limited examples given in class. Consider how the following phrases may cause a misconception or a limitation in understanding.

Explanation	Misconceptions or limitations
1 Cube numbers are the result of multiplying a number by itself three times.	*5 cubed is* $5 \times 5 \times 5 \times 5 = 625$
2 Two negatives will always make a positive.	*There are two negatives here, so the result must be positive:* $-4 + -3 = 7$
3 To divide fractions, keep, flip, change (or KFC).	$$\frac{2}{3} \div 4 = \frac{2}{3} \times 4$$ *There isn't a fraction to flip here, so do I just ignore it?* $$\frac{2}{3} \div 4 = \frac{3}{2} \times 4$$ *Or do I flip the first fraction?*
4 Angles on a straight line always add up to 180°.	*All angles are on a straight line, so* 126°　x°　37° $180 - 126 - 37 = 17$
5 Dividing makes things smaller.	*Doesn't explain* $4 \div 1 = 4$ *and can lead to* $4 \div 0.5 = 2$

Explanation	Misconceptions or limitations
6 For any calculation, we need to use BIDMAS.	$3 \times 4^{6+3} = 12^{6+3} = 12^9 = 5\,159\,780\,352$ *There aren't any brackets, so why would I add 6 and 3 first?* $4 \times 0.21 + 0.21 \times 96 = 21$ *Using BIDMAS here would be long and tedious and obscures the structure of the arithmetic on display. It is worthwhile exploring the distributive law (which would view the calculation as '4 lots of 0.21 + 96 lots of 0.21, or 100 lots of 0.21') especially since pupils are required to use it so much with algebraic terms.*
7 To calculate the mean, add them all up and divide by how many there are.	<table><tr><th>Number of pets</th><th>Frequency</th></tr><tr><td>0</td><td>3</td></tr><tr><td>1</td><td>57</td></tr><tr><td>2</td><td>84</td></tr><tr><td>3</td><td>75</td></tr><tr><td>4</td><td>81</td></tr></table> *(3 + 57 + 84 + 75 + 81) ÷ 5* *Adding up the frequencies is often misunderstood as finding the total, as pupils use their prior knowledge of what they know about the mean.* *They then divide by 5, as there are 5 different classes of data entries listed in the frequency table.*

Often these are said to make things easier for pupils to understand. We need to be careful that, in the pursuit of simplifying our communication, we do not obscure the mathematics. Here are some possible alternative explanations to those above.

1. Cube numbers are the result of multiplying together three copies of an integer.

2. The product of two negative numbers is positive.

3. When dividing by a fraction we can instead multiply by its reciprocal.

4. Angles at a vertex on one side of a straight line always add up to 180°.

5. Dividing by a number between 0 and 1 will increase its magnitude.

6. This one is tricky – we need to spend a lot of time with pupils on the structure of arithmetic, before we mix the four operations together and then finally bring in exponentiation. Brackets itself are difficult – they are not an operation and BIDMAS can confuse this. There are lots of 'hidden brackets' that pupils need to have exposure to like in an exponent $2^{(4+3)}$, or in a radicand $\sqrt{(4+5)}$ or in a fraction $\frac{(10+15)}{(8-3)}$.

7. When we share the total out equally, we call this the mean.

   If we use this explanation from the start, it can remain constant throughout the curriculum with how we find the total slightly changing each time, depending on how the data is presented.

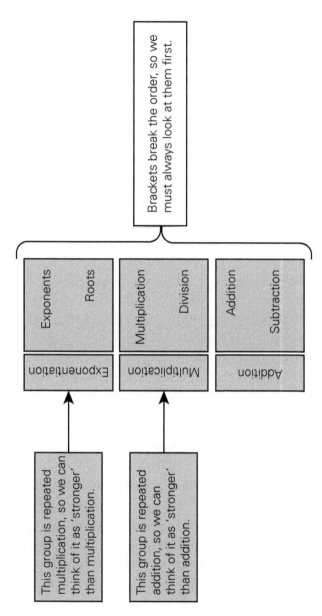

Taken from the OAT Mathematics unit on the order of operations

Writing mathematics

When modelling mathematics it is hugely important that pupils see you writing. When solutions are click-and-play onscreen it can seem as though the mathematics appears like magic and, more importantly, steps in solutions appear at a speed too quick for a learner to properly process. Working out an example 'live' shows pupils how we write mathematics and allows us and them to respond to information in the moment. It forces us to slow down to a pace that pupils can follow and enables us to narrate our internal decision processes. This metacognition, or explaining our thinking, is one part of helping pupils to make sense of new information.

There are many variations of live modelling that can be successful. Standing up and modelling at the whiteboard, using note-writing apps or writing under a visualiser are all approaches that work better than revealing information on a pre-prepared presentation.

When we are modelling, we need to be aware of how we use our board or workspace. We don't want clutter or scribbled bits of information all over a board. We should treat the way we present written mathematics as carefully as we do spoken mathematics and we should train pupils to write their mathematics as clearly as we do. Written mathematics is part of mathematical communication, which we teach alongside the mathematics itself.

If we don't expect pupils to emulate the way we write mathematics we can end up with things that are actually incorrect, such as this 'solution' of the equation $1 + 10x = 7$.

$$1 + 10x = 7 = 10x = 6 = x = 0.6$$

There is a caveat here: doing mathematics is messy and it would be unfair and unnecessary to expect pristine working from your pupils all the time. Such an approach may cause some pupils to be afraid of making mistakes. Insisting on your pupils writing their working in a mathematically correct way is different from being 'neat'. High-quality mathematical communication is something that takes time and effort. Set a plan for building up excellent written mathematics over time that complements the mathematics you are teaching.

Use of exercise books

Exercise books provide a space for pupils to practise. It is important that our pupils use them to rehearse, to iterate and to make mistakes. We should expect them to look after their books (in this, we are teaching responsibility for our things) and it is important that they use them to learn to communicate written mathematics. An exercise book does not, however, make a good revision guide and attempting to make it such is a fool's errand. Once we accept that mathematics is best learnt through practice, and that our exercise books do not provide this after a lesson is finished, we can make sure that lesson time is well spent and that exercise books are well used.

Everything we do in the classroom has an opportunity cost. We should regularly reflect to check whether or not the time spent on any one activity would be time better spent elsewhere. This stands for time pupils spend copying something into their books. There is a place for copying steps of solutions if you use questioning to direct pupils' attention to certain aspects of what they are writing, or if you are giving them space to process what you have shown them. If, however, you ask them to copy solutions down so that they have a record of what they have done – for evidence to observers or for creating a book as a revision guide – then this is time that could be better spent thinking hard and actively engaging in mathematics. No pupil's exercise book will be a better revision guide than those on the market, or than an online platform with teaching videos and endless practice questions.

There are other concerns with asking pupils to copy things into their books. Children write at different rates, so there's always that awkward moment when you are waiting for everyone to finish copying and the ones finished are tempted to start chatting. Moreover, those who will be most disadvantaged by being asked to copy are those who already struggle the most. Repeatedly switching attention from board to book can be disorientating for some pupils, who can lose track of where they got to or struggle to keep up.

The most frequent objection to what we are advocating here is that pupils need examples in their books to support them in independent practice. This concern is null if we leave at least one example on the board for the class to refer to during practice. If we check the understanding of the whole class with mini-whiteboard practice (see Chapter 3) before they start independent work, we should be pretty certain that the first few questions of their independent practice will be completed successfully and if we provide answers to the first few practice questions early on, we can target our support at those who are still struggling to get started.

Vocabulary

Mathematics is full of words that have many meanings, often different outside of mathematics. These are called *polysemous* words. They can be confusing for pupils who might have used or heard these words previously in a different context. Here are a few examples and what pupils may understand by them:

- odd – *strange*

- even – *smooth, straight or equal*

- product – *merchandise or commodities for sale*

- difference – *the quality or condition being different*

- table – *a piece of furniture with a flat top and one or more legs*

- operation – *an act of surgery performed on a patient*

- factor – *a circumstance, fact or influence that contributes to a result*

- expression – *a look on someone's face that conveys a particular emotion*

- prime – *the main or most important thing*

- face – *the front part of a person's head*

- mean – *unkind or unpleasant*

During our exposition, we need to be aware of any polysemous words that are being introduced for the first time and clearly highlight the differences to our pupils. In some cases, the mathematical meaning may be more like the non-mathematical one than we think. (Take 'prime' for example: prime numbers are the fundamental ones for building all the other natural numbers so in some ways they are the most important ones.) When teaching pupils mathematical words, sharing their etymology can help to demystify them, make connections to existing knowledge, and enrich the mathematical experience through history and geography. We mentioned etymology in Chapter 1, using the word 'geometry' as our example. Here are a few examples with those words which begin with the letter p:

parabola   from the Greek *parabole* meaning 'throwing along'. A drawing by Leonardo da Vinci illustrated that the parabola is the trajectory of a projectile fired in a vacuum, a fact proven by Galileo

parallel   from Greek *parallelos* meaning 'along' or 'side by side'

percent   from the Latin phrase *per centum* meaning 'out of a hundred'

polygon   from Greek *poly* meaning 'many' and *gonos* meaning 'angles'

polynomial   from Greek *poly* meaning 'many' and *nomius* meaning 'name'

prime   from Latin *primus* mean 'first'

Pupils can lack the confidence to use these key words in the classroom. This is understandable, as much of the mathematical vocabulary is unlikely to be heard outside the maths classroom and we tend to mispronounce words if we learn them through reading. If we value mathematical literacy, we must provide the opportunity for pupils to practise speaking mathematics – being *consistent* with our own vocabulary and being *insistent* that pupils use the correct language in their responses. Here are some strategies to support you with this:

- **Choral Response:** Pupils can often say powers incorrectly, calling 4^2 *'four with a little 2'* or just *'four two'*. To avoid this, we need to dedicate time for pupils to practise saying the mathematics.

  Consider the image that follows. The teacher points to each power in succession and asks for the pupils to read it out loud in unison. The sequence of powers explicitly shows that some have special names of 'squared' and 'cubed' but that these do not exist for higher exponents. It also exemplifies that there are many ways to say the powers below and they are all mathematically equivalent. Take 17^5. We can say 'the fifth power of 17' *or* '17 to the fifth power' *or* '17 (raised) to the power of 5'.

4^2	2^3	3^2	17^5
3^7	5^8	15^8	5^{18}
5^{17}	17^3	300^2	8^6
$\left(\dfrac{1}{3}\right)^2$	$(-3)^2$	0.3^2	$(-0.3)^2$

- **Think Pair Share:** Ask pupils to think silently or write a response to a prompt or question. Pupils can then share their responses with their neighbouring peers. Reconvene the class and judiciously select pairs to report back on their conversations.

Examples before definitions

It is important that pupils understand the meaning of words, but not so important that they need to memorise a definition. Sometimes definitions require expert knowledge to understand, that is, they only make sense once you know about what they are defining. Here, for instance, is a definition of 'subtend' from Wikipedia.

An angle is subtended by an arc, line segment or any other section of a curve when its two rays pass through the endpoints of that arc, line segment or curve section.

This makes sense to us but for a novice, this is filled with lots of domain-specific vocabulary and can be quite inaccessible. The idea of subtension, however, is quite straightforward when you see it.

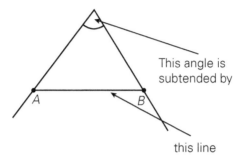

This angle is subtended by

this line

Here is another example, from a possible introduction to standard form.

Today we are learning about standard form. Copy this definition into your exercise books: A number is in standard form if it is written as $x \times 10^n$ where $1 \le x < 10$ and n is an integer.
The number 3×10^2 is in standard form and we are going to write it in ordinary form…

Introducing new vocabulary by presenting the definition on the whiteboard and instructing pupils to copy it down can seem like a good idea, but given the opacity of definitions to novice learners, it is not the best use of time and contradicts our earlier discussion about the importance of high-quality first introductions to a concept. Copying things down is a poor proxy for understanding and more akin to 'busy work'. A definition in a book is not understanding in long-term memory.

Much better is to explore examples and non-examples, so that pupils start to form a picture of what a word or phrase means and, equally importantly, what it does *not* mean.

Today we are learning about standard form. I am going to show you some examples of what standard form is and what it is not. As I show you them, jot down what you notice makes a number in standard form and what does not. At the end, we will talk about what you see.

The number 3×10^{21} is in standard form.
    The number $3 \times 10^{2.1}$ is not in standard form.
The number 3.1×10^2 is in standard form.
    The number 0.31×10^2 is not in standard form.
The number 2.5078×10^9 is in standard form.
    The number $2.5078 \div 10^9$ is not in standard form.
The number 5.607×10^{200} is in standard form.
    The number $5.607 + 10^{200}$ is not in standard form.
The number 3.04×10^{870} is in standard form.
    The number 304×10^{870} is not in standard form.
The number 9.238×10^{-8} is in standard form.
    The number $9.238 \times 10^{-8.2}$ is not in standard form.
The number $9.\dot{9} \times 10^{-32}$ is in standard form.
    The number 10×10^{-32} is not in standard form.

The series of examples and non-examples is revealed one after the other rather than all at once, to avoid overload. The numbers are put in two columns on the board – standard form and not standard form. Each one has been chosen to draw attention to a key characteristic of standard form. Through the use of this sequence and the ensuing discussion, pupils form a clearer mental model of standard form.

Once pupils seem to have a grasp of a concept or word, it is a powerful exercise to ask them to generate their own examples and non-examples. This can be made more challenging by adding constraints to the examples they provide. Consider the following sequence of questions for probing pupils' understanding of 'pentagon' and associated vocabulary.

- Draw a pentagon.

- Draw an **irregular** pentagon.

- Draw an irregular, **concave** pentagon.

- Draw an irregular, concave pentagon that has two perpendicular sides.

What we *don't* say matters

Our tone, expressions and body language are as important as our words. The *way* we talk about mathematics can tell our pupils that it is dull *or* that it is the most inspiring subject in the world. The space we occupy in the classroom can tell our pupils that listening carefully is either essential or optional. The movements we make can be distracting or they can enhance pupils' understanding.

When explaining things to pupils, we should consider where we are in the classroom. If we are walking round the room as we talk, or are busy distributing worksheets, we can make it harder for pupils to focus on what we are saying. We should address our audience clearly and with eye contact. Standing in the same place can, with time, indicate to pupils that they need to get ready to listen when we enter that space.

In *Annie Murphy Paul's The Extended Mind in Action*, Turner et al. (2022) draw on the work of Manuela Macedonia to teach us that *'gestures improve spatial thinking and advance our understanding of complex concepts, as well as reduce our cognitive load and improve our memory. How we script and intentionally use gestures to accompany our explanations and how we then encourage our pupils to integrate these movements into their own gestural lexicon can have a huge impact. Gesture has the power to make the discrete and linear verbal explanation into a rich 3D understanding of complex concepts using our ancestral shared native language.'* (p. 35)

Skilled mathematics teachers frequently use simple gestures in their teaching. Using your body to demonstrate movement or space reinforces your words and gives pupils another 'way in' to the material. Used consistently, pupils recognise what you mean by your actions. Here are some examples of effective gesture to reinforce mathematical ideas.

- When teaching negative numbers, pupils need to remember the action of flipping tiles/counters for the additive inverse of a number (more on this in Chapter 4). To emphasise this action, we can place our palms open facing the ceiling and turn them over, repeatedly, whenever we say, 'additive inverse'.

- When explaining that vertically opposite angles are equal, we straighten our arms and cross one over the other.

- When talking about perpendicular lines, we can place our arms straight, crossing at a 90° angle. For parallel lines, we can place our arms straight in parallel.

- When teaching the cosine rule we explain that we need to know side-angle-side (SAS) to find the missing side. We emphasise the angle being 'trapped' and recreate the image with our thumb and forefinger.

- Whenever teaching angles, we must emphasise the dynamic nature of a turn (which is not communicated in static images) so that pupils understand what an angle is really measuring. We can place our pen on one side and turn it through an angle on the page, or use our arm in the same way on a board at the front. Done consistently, pupils will associate the turning with angles that they see printed.

Our non-verbal communication extends to the impression we leave on pupils. When we are firm, we tell them that we have high expectations of their behaviour and participation. When we are warm, we tell them that our classroom is a safe place. When we are enthusiastic about mathematics, we tell them that our subject is worth investing in. Being a reflective practitioner allows us to improve *what* we say and *what* we write, but the glue that transforms these parts into something beautiful is *how* we are in the classroom.

Chapter Summary

In this chapter, we have explored some of the many practices and ideas that make up classroom instruction.

- Use worked examples in ways that optimise their utility, thinking carefully about your numbers, your explanations and where you want pupils' attention to be.
- Model the mathematics live so pupils see it being written.
- Create opportunities for pupils to speak the mathematics as often as possible.
- Introducing a novel concept with a definition can be confusing for pupils. Instead use examples and non-examples so pupils can explore what something is and what something isn't.
- Everything has an opportunity cost. Make sure pupils spend their time thinking hard and actively engaging in mathematics.

FURTHER READING

Michael Pershan *Teaching Math with Examples* (2021). A book that highlights the importance of examples, drawing from extensive research to clearly describe some practical ways we can make the most of them in the mathematics classroom.

Emma McCrea *Making Every Maths Lesson Count: Six principles to support great maths teaching* (2019). Full of accessible and practical ideas that can be implemented into your classroom that very same day.

Craig Barton *How I Wish I'd Taught Maths* (2018). Detailing his 12 years of mistakes and what he now does differently, with his wealth of knowledge from talking to other experts and reflecting on research. It is a brilliant introduction to the world of cognitive science and how this can be translated into the mathematics classroom.

Craig Barton *Reflect, Expect, Check, Explain* (2020). Drawing from research, this book details clearly the techniques we can use in the classroom to provoke and deepen mathematical thinking – preventing pupils from simply moving on to the next question once they have reached the answer.

Tom Sherrington *Rosenshine's Principles in Action* (2019a). A concise booklet that details Barak Rosenshine's Principles of Instruction; demonstrating how they can be put into practice in everyday classrooms. A short, yet incredibly influential read.

Tom Bennett *Running the Room* (2020). An easy to read and honest account of what can go wrong inside many classrooms, offering clear behaviour strategies and advice for all teachers to implement.

Chris Bills, Liz Bills, Anne Watson & John Mason *Thinkers* (2018). A brilliant collection of activities to elicit mathematical thinking, which can be used across a wide range of topics within mathematics – regardless of whether the pupil is in Key Stage 2 or studying their A Levels.

Siegfried Engelmann and Douglas Carnine *Theory of Instruction: Principles and applications* (1991). A seminal work on the power of quality direct instruction in the mathematics classroom.

3

Responsive teaching

First coined by education researcher Dylan Wiliam, 'responsive teaching' sums up what great teachers do on a daily basis: finding out what their pupils already know and teaching them from there (to paraphrase Ausubel (1968): *'The most important single factor influencing learning is what the pupil already knows. Ascertain this and teach him accordingly.'*). Responsive teaching is about a constant process of formative assessment and adjustment of our instruction, to meet the needs of the pupils we teach. It is a process that needs to be integrated into the entirety of our teaching practice – curriculum, planning learning, classroom practice and assessment. In this book there are chapters on each of these things; in this chapter we will look at them all through the lens of responsive teaching.

In Chapter 1 we introduced the storytelling metaphor for planning curriculum and learning sequences. In this metaphor, responsive teaching is where our story turns into a detective novel. In order to ascertain what the pupil already knows, we must be detectives, asking questions and gathering evidence. In responding to the evidence that we find, our detective work becomes essential. A classroom mindset of openness and curiosity underpins being a responsive teacher.

Curriculum and planning

Curriculum is the entirety of the experiences that we offer pupils at school. The mathematics curriculum should be planned to provide opportunities for teachers to formatively assess their pupils and respond to what they learn. Any curriculum that insists that a teacher move on to the next lesson whether the pupils have 'got it' or not is inherently inflexible and in opposition to the idea of responsive teaching. Each class is different, a collection of around 30 individuals with different needs and prior knowledge. It is far better to work through learning at a pace that suits your class than to rush through content without developing understanding. Every lesson should start from where the pupils are at, rather than where we *think* the pupils *should* be at.

Formative and summative assessment

A formative assessment is any check for understanding or fluency that helps to shape the direction of travel and should be thought of in contrast to summative assessment, which measures what has been learned at points along the route.

A planned curriculum will always include time for summative assessment. Summative assessments are useful for monitoring and checking, as we discuss in Chapter 9. They allow us to gather data with a snapshot of a cohort's knowledge at the time of the assessment and to report on that information. They can highlight gaps in the curriculum or areas for development in our pedagogy. Summative assessments tend to feel significant to pupils and they often prioritise them. We must be aware that summative assessment takes up curriculum time and contributes to teacher workload. Too much of it does not contribute to learning and can have a negative effect on outcomes.

Summative and formative assessments may not really differ in the questions they contain; it is what we do with the information we gain that makes an assessment summative or formative. A formative assessment helps us to connect new knowledge to pupils' existing knowledge or to provide pre-teaching if we find gaps.

For example, if we are planning to teach a unit on fraction, decimal and percentage equivalences, we need to ascertain what our pupils know in order to increase their chances of learning the new material well. One of the ways we could collect this evidence is to use a pre-test, whose purpose would be to inform our planning. It could be delivered at the beginning of the unit, or a few lessons before, so that we have an opportunity to respond to the information it gives us. It might include questions about how fractions are represented, equivalent fractions, division, place value, multiplying by powers of ten, and use different representations (such as a number line or bar model) to check how familiar they are to the class.

Below is an example of a pre-test for a unit on fractions and percentages of an amount. Take a moment to consider why each question might be useful and what misconceptions they might expose.

How we respond to a pre-test depends on how it goes. If all pupils do well, the unit can proceed as planned. Complications come when, as is most likely, you get a mixed response to the pre-test. If the vast majority of the class require a reteach of the prerequisite knowledge, then do that. Make sure that the few pupils who are secure in this knowledge have questions that deepen their understanding, so that we are not wasting their time. If it is a minority of pupils who need intervention, do this another way, such as a small group intervention and online homework with videos and practice questions.

1. How many squares would you need to shade $\frac{1}{4}$ on this shape to shade $\frac{1}{4}$ of the whole shape?	2. What fraction of this shape is shaded?	3. Find $\frac{1}{7}$ of £70	4. Calculate 10% of £60
a. 3 b. 4 c. 5 d. 6	a. $\frac{1}{4}$ b. $\frac{1}{5}$ c. You cannot tell. d. $\frac{1}{3}$	a. 7 b. 10 c. 490 d. 11	a. £0.60 b. £6.00 c. 60p d. 6p
5. There are an equal number of bricks in two towers. Tower A is made from blocks that are $\frac{2}{3}$ red. Tower B is made from blocks that are $\frac{1}{3}$ red. Which tower is shorter? a. Tower A b. You cannot tell c. Tower B d. Same height	6. Which of these is equal to 40%? a. 0.4 b. $\frac{2}{5}$ c. 0.040 d. $\frac{40}{100}$	7. What is 9% as a decimal? a. 0.9 b. 0.09 c. 9.0 d. $\frac{9}{100}$	8. Calculate 30% of 300 a. 30 b. 10 c. 90 d. 100

Example pre-test for fractions and percentages of an amount

9. Write 75% as a fraction in its simplest form. a. $\frac{4}{10}$ b. $\frac{75}{100}$ c. $\frac{3}{4}$ d. $\frac{15}{75}$	10. Find $\frac{3}{5}$ of 30 a. 10 b. 6 c. 18 d. 50	11. What is $\frac{6}{20}$ as a percentage? a. 6% b. 3% c. 30% d. 0.3%	12. 35% of 135 is…? a. 54 b. 40.5 c. 13.5 d. 45
13. What is 1.3 as a percentage? a. 13% b. 1.3% c. 130% d. 30%	14. Hayley has 30 cakes. She eats 6 of them. What percentage of the cakes has she eaten? a. 80% b. 20% c. 5% d. 120%	15. Find 25% of 600 cars a. 100 cars b. 75 cars c. 150 cars d. 125 cars	16. Convert this fraction into a decimal $\frac{3}{8}$ a. 2.666 b. 3.8 c. 0.375 d. 0.38

Example pre-test for fractions and percentages of an amount

There is no need to spend a long time meticulously marking pre-tests, or to record any results, if the purpose of the pre-test is to inform planning. You might put the test in piles sorted by common mistakes, for instance. Reading through the tests and making notes on any relevant findings is enough. What the test tells you is what pupils could remember when they took it. It does not mean that they haven't covered the content before, and it may well be in their long-term memory somewhere, ready to be recalled with the right priming. Be careful what inferences you make from any assessment – don't overstretch what you can tell from it.

Formative assessment is not limited to checking prerequisite knowledge. We need to plan for how we can ascertain if pupils are making sense of the learning throughout a lesson. One way of doing so is to ask the whole class a question at key points during the lesson. These 'hinge questions' can be very useful to help you check how effective instruction has been to that point. If you ask the right question to the whole class at the right time, you will know if the class is ready to get started on independent practice or to move on and, if the question is carefully designed, it can alert you to any misconceptions the pupils have developed.

When planning a sequence of learning, decide which questions will show you if a pupil understands the aspect of the topic you are exploring. A great place to go to for hinge questions is the website *Diagnostic Questions* by Craig Barton, which we also mentioned in Chapter 2. Here you will find multiple-choice questions (MCQs) on most areas of mathematics, with answers carefully designed to expose common misconceptions. We might use MCQs in a starter activity, to check if the pupils have the prerequisite knowledge needed for the lesson. We might use them as hinge questions to check for understanding after a period of whole-class instruction, or we might use them to see whether or not we can move onto the next section of learning.

Here is a multiple-choice question intended to expose misconceptions around the magnitude of fractions.

What is the missing fraction?

$$\frac{3}{5} < \boxed{}$$

a) $\frac{3}{7}$ b) $\frac{7}{10}$ c) $\frac{2}{5}$ d) $\frac{12}{20}$

The incorrect answers, or distractors, here highlight different mistakes. Answer a) uses the same numerator but has a larger denominator. If a pupil chooses this one, they might think that a larger denominator means a larger number. This misconception could be addressed with a pictorial representation, such as bar models, to show that $\frac{1}{7}$ is smaller than $\frac{1}{5}$. The answer b) is correct, and would probably be chosen after pupils had found that $\frac{6}{10}$ is equivalent to $\frac{3}{5}$. A pupil who chooses answer c) might have confusion over how to read the inequality symbol. Answer d) is equivalent to $\frac{3}{5}$. A pupil choosing this might mistakenly think that the larger numbers in the numerator and denominator suggest a larger number overall.

Responding to the evidence we gather from hinge questions can be a challenging part of responsive teaching. It is difficult and takes great confidence to alter your lesson plan in the moment, so we should plan to respond. If you are not yet confident with thinking on your feet, anticipate what could happen and plan accordingly. When designing or choosing a hinge question, you will have thought about the possible misconceptions that a pupil could have and used them to write the question. As you are thinking about these misconceptions, decide how you would respond, remembering that you will be acting in the moment. If there are very few correct answers, quickly scan the answers that the pupils have given. You may like to discuss, in general terms, why this answer is not correct. *'Let's look at a). What was the person answering this question thinking? What mistake did they make? What did they muddle up?'* This allows pupils to think through and acknowledge their misconceptions. It also allows those who got the question correct to continue to think about the question and learn more about the structure of the mathematics as they learn how others have approached it.

You may then put some similar questions up on the board, do one as a narrated worked example, then ask the pupils to practise the rest. You may then wish to ask a similar hinge question again, to see if pupils are continuing to hold the same misconceptions or if they have gained some insight from your remedial work.

Hinge questions are often used to check if pupils are ready to work independently. At this point, you might want to use several, one at a time. Scan the room and note mentally, or on a laminated seating plan, who is getting which question incorrect. This will tell you who will need support during the independent work. It might indicate to you to create a small group of pupils and reteach a particular aspect of the work. If enough pupils are not getting the work correct, then you might decide to reteach, do more worked examples or guided practice with everyone.

If you are unable to find a hinge question that is appropriate for your lesson, or you would like to challenge yourself, you can write your own. The best way to do this is to collaborate with your colleagues to think of the most common or problematic misconceptions that pupils could hold at that particular point in the lesson. Start with the misconceptions and build the question from there.

If we go back to fraction, decimal and percentage equivalence, we might want to design a hinge question for the point where we are converting terminating decimals into fractions. After modelling using different representations and guided practice, we will need to check if the pupils are ready to work independently and see who might need additional support. We could ask a simple question such as, *'Convert 0.3 to a fraction.'* To get the correct answer, pupils will need to understand place value so that they know that the digit '3' has a value of 3 tenths and is written as a fraction as $\frac{3}{10}$, or they would need to recognise that 0.3 is 3 ÷ 10 and write this as a fraction. An alternative would be to consider the misconceptions a pupil might have. Some might think that the digit '3' represents thirds and give the answer $\frac{1}{3}$. They could use the digits given in the decimal 0.3 to create $\frac{0}{3}$ or they could place the 3 in the the 100 column (having thought about percentages recently) and give the answer $\frac{3}{100}$. If we use these as our distractor answers in a multiple-choice question, then we not only discover who can answer the question correctly, but also what mistakes those who cannot answer it correctly make. In both cases, we are asking one question, but we learn a lot more from the MCQ than we do from the question on its own, thus the MCQ is more useful for formative assessment.

There are some things to be aware of when using hinge questions. Pupils can make calculation errors that do not necessarily mean that they hold significant misconceptions. Try to eliminate the possibility of these slip-ups by designing the questions and possible responses accordingly. In our example above, it is unlikely that any of the answers would be obtained through a calculation error. We should also consider the way these questions are administered in light of the purpose of the assessment. The purpose of hinge questions is to inform you what your pupils know, or don't know, so that you can make a decision as to what to do next. You should use mini-whiteboards or some form of voting so that you can see the results very quickly from the whole class. There is more on these techniques in Chapter 2.

If we rely on questioning individuals at these key points in a lesson, we may happen upon the only three pupils in the room that are ready to move on or, if we rely on volunteers, the pupils who are confident and comfortable to answer in front of everyone else. We really don't know what everyone else is thinking. If a small minority of pupils in the class are asked the majority of the questions, then formative assessment loses its efficacy. Even when we use devices to help with this – cold-calling, lollypop sticks, random person selectors – we still only know what one pupil is thinking at a time. For formative assessment, a census is always better than a sample.

The next part of the lesson where we can gather evidence is while the pupils are working independently. Walk around the class and listen in to pupils talking about the work. Circulating and marking in the moment will give you more information to ascertain where the general level of understanding is, as well as that of specific pupils, although it is a less efficient method of collecting information than whole-class responses and should be used as one small part in a suite of evidence.

At the end of a lesson, we can use quick checks in the form of 'exit tickets' to inform what happens in the next lesson. An exit ticket comprises of a few carefully selected questions, ideally increasing in difficulty, which will let you know what pupils still need to practise and where their proficiency breaks down. Its purpose is to help you decide where to begin the learning in the next lesson, therefore it should try to find the limits of pupils' understanding. If an exit ticket is too easy and all pupils get all questions correct, you might feel successful, but it won't tell you much (unless to confirm that you can move on). Similarly, if the questions are too difficult and very few pupils can answer them, then it might look like the pupils have learned nothing. This hopefully isn't true: appropriately pitched questions with progressive difficulty should provide the information you need to prepare your next lesson. Be aware that an exit ticket does not show long-term learning or understanding over initial mimicry, but initial mimicry is a first step towards long-term learning.

When we respond to exit tickets, we should again remind ourselves of their purpose. They are usually used to give us a clue as to what the pupils understood in the lesson and whether or not they are ready to move on. As such, their purpose is to help us prepare our next lesson. Using exit tickets should be quick and efficient as you could be doing it several times a day. Do them on a piece of paper (not in pupils' books). As you go through them, quickly sort them into three categories, 'all correct', 'none correct' and 'bit of both', or group them by misconception – this pile got this bit wrong, this pile got that bit wrong. If you have a large pile of 'all correct' it might be worth reviewing the questions you have used: were they the right questions to expose possible misconceptions or was your teaching just so amazing, and the pupils so attentive, that everyone got it?

Look at the other piles, what the pupils were unable to do and use this to inform your next lesson. You may use a starter to practise where there is a small error. You may wish to reteach the content using a different approach, model or manipulative. You could use carefully considered worked examples and guided practice while allowing some pupils to work independently. Point out the errors that were made in general terms, *'This is where pupils learning this often go wrong…'* If you have a class you share with another teacher, share this work with the other teacher as part of your handover.

When you are talking to pupils about their misconceptions, never reveal any irritation or annoyance. It is normal while learning to make errors, to forget, to misunderstand and for minds to wander and miss things. Let the pupils know that this is the case. We can reassure them that, if they never make mistakes, then we are not stretching them enough; it is our job to find out what they understand then push them past this. Tell them why we revisit the same ideas again and again. Make sure they know why you want them to complete pre-tests, answer hinge questions and do exit tickets: you need to understand where they are on the learning journey so that you can plan and adapt lessons to meet their needs.

Adaptive teaching

Responsive teaching aims to work with pupils to take them from where they are in their understanding and develop their learning from that point. We do this by considering their prior knowledge and experience and teach them accordingly. This approach is the right of all pupils, including those of different prior attainment, those who learn at a different rate, and those who special educational needs or disabilities (SEND). All our pupils are individuals who we must get to know.

The 'label' that some pupils may have, as a result of a professional diagnosis, gives you a heads-up that you may well have to make certain adaptations for them but, as each pupil is unique, there is never a one-size-fits-all approach to making sure they can access the learning. Labelling pupils by diagnosis or perceived ability level can lead to us planning lessons that limit pupils or exclude them from potential learning experiences. One pupil with autistic spectrum disorder (ASD), for example, will present with different behaviours to another and therefore may have different needs. Statements such as, *'autistic pupils must have rigid routines'* could be true but will not be for all. We must get to know pupils as individuals and adapt our teaching accordingly.

When we receive information about our pupils with SEND, it is often focused on the difficulties they face. In general, the guidance and advice given is on behavioural aspects of classroom practice, such as, *'sit near the front,'* or, *'allow extra time for processing'*. Over and above this, we must use our specialist, mathematics-specific pedagogical knowledge to focus on the teaching and learning processes that will create an inclusive classroom for all, allowing every pupil to access the mathematics they need to be successful in education.

It would be easy to become completely overwhelmed at the thought of tailoring your teaching to meet the needs of every pupil that you teach. Indeed, complete personalisation is impossible unless we are doing one-to-one tutoring. However, the more that we plan for and deliver high-quality, inclusive teaching, the less we will need to plan specific interventions for individual pupils. What works for those with SEND will also help all pupils. In Chapter 4 we explore the power of multiple representations in depth, but here we must say that that a teacher who understands ways of representing mathematics beyond the symbolism of number and algebra creates a more inclusive curriculum.

To make mathematics accessible, breaking down learning into small, coherent steps is essential. Very explicit teaching of new ideas and procedures is important for pupils who struggle to access mathematics and is an example of a 'strategy' that helps certain groups of pupils but which, actually, benefits all. Clear modelling with worked examples, and opportunities for pupils to try a process or discuss an idea, before starting on independent practice, are key (something like 'My Turn'/'Your Turn' is an example of this). Provide explicit instructions and prompts, but don't waste time forcing pupils to write these out in their books (this is exhausting for some pupils and pointless for most, as we saw in Chapter 2). Use guided practice – a structured exercise with gradually disappearing instructions and prompts – to lead pupils to a feeling of success. These do not always need to be prepared in advance, as we can write prompts out on the board for those who need it while others work independently through the questions.

Backwards-fading is a brilliant technique for reducing cognitive load on pupils for those who need it. The steps of finding a solution are set out apart from the very last one, then in the next question, one step is removed from the end, then in the next another step removed, until pupils are completing the whole process on their own. Here is an example of a set of questions using backwards-fading. Notice how pupils working on these will be gradually moved towards completing a multi-step procedure rather than being expected to do it all from the start.

Target those pupils in class who you know will need extra support. Make sure there are calculators available for those who struggle with basic mental or written calculations, when the content of the lesson does not depend on it. For something like learning about angle facts, poor mental arithmetic puts up an artificial barrier to learning the concept at hand, so remove the barrier. Obviously, fluency of calculation should be developed and practised another time.

Using appropriate praise in the classroom is very important. Praise the correct parts of any response and correct any errors or misconceptions. Do not say, *'Well done'* to an incorrect response for two reasons: it reinforces misconceptions and devalues praise. Get to know your pupils as some are embarrassed by public acknowledgment.

Fill in the blanks to decompose these numbers as products of prime factors.

a. 50 = 5 × 10

    = 5 × 5 × _____

    = _____ × ____^{2}

b. 20 = 2 × 10

    = 2 × _____ × _____

    = _____ ____^{2} × _____

c. 100 = 10 × 10

    = _____ × _____ × _____ × _____

    = _____ ____^{2} × ____^{2}

d. 88 = 8 ×

    = _____ × _____ × 11

    = _____ × _____ × _____ × 11

    =

e. 42 = _____ • _____

    = _____ • _____ • _____

f. 420 = _____ • _____

    =

Example of backwards-fading

Some pupils need an adapted curriculum where practical changes, such as a larger font size or coloured paper, are made to the materials and the environment so that a child can access the mathematics. This is different from an adaptive curriculum, where you are able to make changes based on what happens in the classroom. Perhaps you need to spend more time on something than intended, or you need to go back to spend some time on building blocks that pupils are missing, or you need to work with manipulatives for longer. A truly inclusive, adaptive curriculum will allow you to do this, enabling the short cycle of assessment and response that you carry out in every lesson.

When adapting teaching, be wary of creating different tasks or activities for different pupils. Expecting some pupils to reach a lower level than others before a lesson even begins is the opposite of having high expectations and supporting pupils to reach them. Only in rare circumstances should pupils be given different work instead of reasonable adjustments being made. For a number of years, using worksheets labelled bronze/silver/gold or red/amber/green was advocated as a good way to differentiate to meet the needs of different pupils in a class. The problem with this approach is that the practice on the 'gold' or 'green' level is generally essential practice for any pupil who wants to approach mastery of a topic. If only the quickest pupils get the chance to reach it, only they will have a chance of achieving highly. If some pupils start on these 'top' levels, they can miss out on foundational practice that embeds the core of a process or idea. Over time, the compounding effect of always working on 'bronze' or 'red' is guaranteed lower attainment and, potentially, low levels of self-worth when it comes to mathematics. If we have the mindset that with the right conditions, scaffolding and time pupils can access most activities, then we should not have predetermined, fixed ideas of where pupils can progress to.

Using teaching assistants

Teaching assistants (TAs) are used in secondary classrooms to support the inclusion of pupils with special educational needs or disabilities. They are a valuable resource who can contribute hugely to the success of your lessons and can provide extra insight into misconceptions, difficulties and successes that pupils are experiencing.

In our busy work week, it can be too easy to forget to include TAs in the planning process and they may arrive at our lesson without even knowing the topic we are working on. The Education Endowment Foundation (2018) has made evidence-based recommendations into the best use of TAs in primary and secondary schools. The first four of these recommendations relate to working with TAs in everyday classrooms:

- TAs should not be used as an informal teaching resource for low-attaining pupils.

- Use TAs to add value to what teachers do, not replace them.

- Use TAs to help pupils develop independent learning skills and manage their own learning.

- Ensure TAs are fully prepared for their role in the classroom.

While the way in which TAs are deployed is down to school leadership, these recommendations relate directly to our role as a mathematics teacher. Make sure that, as far as is reasonably possible, teaching assistants are included in department professional development time. If you are discussing the representations and tasks you will use in a unit of work, it makes sense that any adult working with our pupils are familiar with them and that they understand why we use them. It is essential that we are all using the agreed language and shared approaches. It would be a huge advantage if TAs were knowledgeable on how learning typically progresses through different areas of mathematics, particularly the early acquisition of fundamentals, such as concept of number, place value and calculation.

The SEND department should have access to all your curriculum documents and can work with you to ensure any necessary adaptations are made for individual pupils. Make sure you share your planning with any teaching assistants who will be in your lessons. This should not involve additional workload or necessitate a written document. It could be that TAs are part of your collaborative planning sessions, or that you have an informal conversation about what you intend to teach in the following week and how you are going to approach the topic. In this discussion, ask TAs to provide you with information on the barriers that pupils may face and offer solutions on how to scaffold the learning for them.

Most importantly, you will work together in your classroom to ensure that all pupils can access the mathematics. As the teacher in the class, you are responsible for directing the other adults involved. A TA is another pair of eyes and ears to help with the detective work involved in responsive teaching. Make sure they are briefed on what hinge questions you will be using and what possible misconceptions you are looking out for; TAs can offer you useful feedback that will help you respond in the lesson and adapt future planning.

Feedback

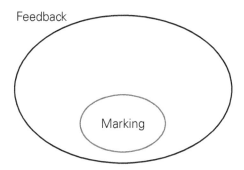

Marking ≠ Feedback

In this quasi-Venn diagram, the universal set is all the different types of feedback we can give. Marking is a small subset of this and only one of the strands of evidence that we use to discover more about how our pupils are learning. By looking at their work, we can gain insight into pupils' understanding of an area of mathematics, but marking books can become so time-consuming that its usefulness is outweighed by its arduousness.

There are certain types of marking in mathematics that definitely lose the arduous/useful battle. 'Tick and flick' is quick(ish) but pointless. Writing comments on work done two weeks ago is arduous for little learning gain – there is little to be achieved in pupils responding to something the teacher has written on a piece of work from a topic they are no longer studying.

Where possible, all work should be 'marked', but pupils can tick or cross their own answers in a very short time during the lesson, allowing you to focus on the things that they are getting wrong and to adapt lesson time accordingly. If you use exit tickets (as discussed earlier in the chapter), they do not need to be marked extensively. Ticks and crosses, with circles for omissions, will suffice provided you respond to what you learn from them by determining the direction of the next lesson.

Feedback, done right, serves two purposes: the teacher will know what to do next, and the pupil will develop their understanding in some way. Any marking should serve one of these purposes, otherwise it is a waste of time and should not be done.

Throughout this chapter we have seen that responsive teaching involves forensically collecting information on how our pupils are getting on. The information we collect is useless if it doesn't prompt a change in our teaching or a gain in pupils' understanding. Formative assessment is not assessment *of* learning; it is assessment *for* learning. Responsive teaching is using every tool at our disposal to teach pupils the right things at the right time.

Chapter Summary

In this introduction to responsive teaching we have explored some important ideas and how they can be used in the classroom.

- Responsive teaching is a constant process of formative assessment and adjustment of our teaching practice to meet the needs of our pupils.
- Use pre-tests, hinge questions and exit tickets to gather information and then respond accordingly.
- Don't make assumptions about pupils' capabilities.
- Teaching assistants are key members of your team. Include them in CPD, consider them when planning, keep them informed and use them in formative assessment.
- Marking is a small part of feedback. If it is not useful, don't do it.

FURTHER READING

Responsive Teaching: cognitive science and formative assessment in practice by Harry Fletcher-Wood (2018) is full of strategies for improving formative assessment across subjects.

The Inclusive Classroom by Daniel Sobel and Sara Alston (2021) discusses how we can use practices that do not disadvantage students.

4

Representing mathematics

One of the aims of the curriculum is to develop procedural fluency alongside conceptual understanding. The National Curriculum would like all pupils to *'become fluent in the fundamentals of mathematics, including through varied and frequent practice with increasingly complex problems over time, so that pupils develop conceptual understanding and the ability to recall and apply knowledge rapidly and accurately'.* This fluency and flexibility of knowledge allows pupils to know when to use a particular procedure, use it efficiently and accurately and apply it in unfamiliar situations. If a pupil has a conceptual understanding they are less likely to forget how to perform an operation as they can draw on the fundamental meaning of the mathematics.

Children's initial ideas about number are based on physical items, counting and sorting. Children in their early years of education count physical items to help them understand the 'oneness of one' or the 'twoness of two' and to compare the relative size of numbers. We move pupils to represent numbers in drawings and then in symbols – digits written according to certain rules to make numerals – the numerals being the most abstract representation of the number. It is the development of the relationship between these representations that begins the understanding of what a number is. This use of concrete manipulatives and pictorial representations alongside symbols (digits and letters) to represent mathematical concepts is always important, not just in the early years but all through secondary school and beyond. Being able to access abstract concepts in multiple ways gives pupils more ways into the mathematics, increasing their chances of understanding.

Jean Piaget, Zoltan Dienes and Jerome Bruner all describe, in different ways, how children begin to understand abstract mathematical concepts and their symbolic representations after they experience ideas in a concrete form (see, for example, Piaget, 1967 or Dienes, 1961). Every one of us needs to have a mental model in place in order to think about an abstract mathematical concept, and we all have our own mental models to explain the mathematics to ourselves and to make connections between different concepts. Our pupils are no different, except that they are more novice than us. This means that their mental models are less likely to be robust or accurate, especially if they are only presented with the symbolic representations of numerals and letters. Using concrete manipulatives and pictorial models in our teaching helps us to represent and scaffold concepts as they are introduced. They provide a bridge between ideas, allowing pupils to make connections between otherwise seemingly unconnected areas of mathematics, so strengthening their mathematical schema. In this chapter, we will show you why multiple representations help pupils to attain greater understanding.

In Chapter 1, we discussed the difference between mathematics subject knowledge and mathematics-specific pedagogical knowledge, and we saw that *teaching* mathematics is different from *doing* mathematics. It might seem obvious to say it, but a novice's understanding is not the same as an expert's understanding, which means that things we see, or that are obvious to us, will not be seen by our pupils and will not be obvious to them. We think about mathematics in a fundamentally different way to the pupils in our class. In his book *Why Don't Pupils Like School?* (2021) cognitive scientist Daniel Willingham tells us that our minds prefer the concrete to the abstract. The concrete makes more sense to us as it links more readily to what we already know. The concrete, however, does not transfer like the abstract, and hence abstraction should be 'the goal of schooling'. Willingham explains that we *'understand new things in the context of things we already know and most of what we know is concrete'*. Our pedagogical road map, therefore, involves taking pupils on a journey from the limited concrete understanding they have of mathematical concepts to a flexible abstract understanding. Concrete manipulatives, pictorial models and mathematical symbols help us to build that journey in a coherent way. We explore the idea of coherence further in Chapter 9 but before we get there, we need to take a closer look at the mathematical representations we have at our disposal.

Concrete-pictorial-abstract approach

The concrete-pictorial-abstract (CPA) approach came from work by the psychologist Jerome Bruner in his 1966 book, *Toward a Theory of Instruction.* Bruner called his concept *'enactive-iconic-symbolic modes of representation'*. The approach was adopted in the late 1970s by the Singapore Ministry of Education who called it the concrete-pictorial-abstract approach to teaching mathematics. Different modes of representation are ways of making sense of content at various levels (up to quite advanced school mathematics) and should not be seen as age-related or ability-related. Concrete manipulatives are used alongside pictorial representations and symbolic notation, and as pupils become increasingly proficient in the latter, the concrete and pictorial representations are gradually faded away.

An important understanding here is that symbolic representations are the most efficient and transferable representations we have in mathematics, but they are not sufficient for most pupils to make sense of abstract concepts. Concrete and pictorial representations help more pupils make meaning, but they have limitations. By understanding that concrete, pictorial and symbolic representations are increasingly flexible representations of underlying abstract concepts, we can use them as a means of increasingly sophisticated communication of mathematics. (Although CPA is the commonly understood acronym for the approach we are talking about in this chapter, we are using the phrase 'concrete-pictorial-symbolic' throughout, since it is important to understand that all three represent abstract concepts in increasingly efficient and transferable ways.)

We have seen that we must represent mathematics in order to communicate it. The mathematics community has developed conventional ways to do this with numerals, symbols and domain-specific language, and fluency in these is part of the goal we aim for. Using concrete manipulatives and pictorial models alongside the conventional symbolic representations will expose the underlying structure and help the pupils to 'see' the mathematics that they are doing, moving them towards the goal. Throughout the rest of this chapter, we will briefly explore some of the most commonly used representations available to us. Look at the Further reading at the end of the chapter for more detailed sources of information.

Concrete and pictorial (algebra tiles)	Pictorial and symbolic (multiplication grid)	Symbolic
		$(x + 1)(x + 2)$ $\equiv x^2 + 3x + 2$

abstract concept: multiplication (of expressions containing variables)

Concrete, pictorial and symbolic representations of an abstract concept

Commonly-used pictorial representations

The number line

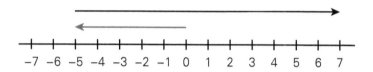

The number line is one of the most crucial representations. It is the only representation mentioned in the National Curriculum. It is hard to find a mathematics classroom without one and many people still hold this image in their head when calculating with positive and negative numbers. Once concepts of ordinality and cardinality have been explored and established with young pupils, the number line is an excellent model to pupils' understanding of number and symmetry about zero.

The number line representation has the advantage of being used throughout primary and secondary school and so is familiar to most pupils. Using it means that there are none of the difficulties associated with using an unfamiliar representation for a novel concept. The number line can be used to represent integers, rational and irrational numbers. It can be used to model arithmetic with positive and negative numbers, inequalities and rounding and is a place to introduce vectors in one dimension. Once we move to algebra, the number line appears horizontally and vertically as part of the Cartesian grid and is used to represent number relationships in graphs and vectors in two dimensions (and then onto three).

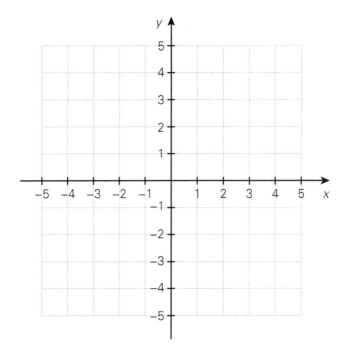

Double number line and ratio tables

A double number line consists of two number lines, one above the other. The lines are aligned at zero and have different scales and, as a result, can be used to represent proportional (multiplicative) relationships. Any area of the curriculum that involves proportional reasoning can be represented with a double number line. Since the lines have different scales, we can imagine that one has been 'stretched' against the other, and this stretch is a scale factor or constant of proportionality.

Any multiplication between values on the top line is directly mirrored between values on the bottom line. Similarly, the multiplication between lines works anywhere along them.

Below is a double number line linking distance and time, where the constant of proportionality is the speed of travel.

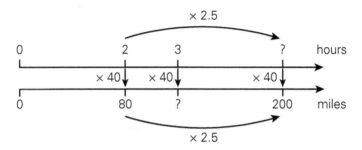

As pupils develop an understanding of multiplication as scaling and understand that in a directly proportional relationship both zeros align, the double number line can be developed into a ratio table (see below).

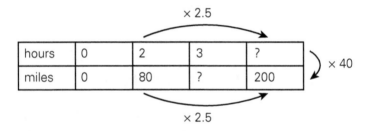

This is a more efficient representation to use, especially with large numbers, although some of the scaling structure is lost. The ratio table can be further contracted to show a proportion diagram such as the one below. This diagram makes it very easy to see both the functional multiplier (constant of proportionality, vertically) and the scalar multiplier (horizontally).

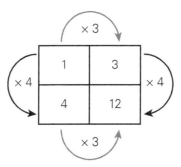

All these representations communicate that multiplication happens in 'both directions' and help pupils to pick the easiest multiplication in each context.

The area model

An area model is used to represent multiplication and division and exposes factors. It shows how the laws of arithmetic (commutativity, associativity and distributivity) apply to numbers and algebraic expressions.

One of the ways that multiplication is represented to young pupils is with an array, whereby a collection of counters is organised into a rectangular arrangement, for example:

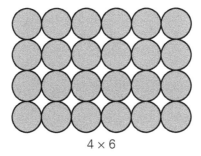

4 × 6

This can be developed into the area model for multiplication, which is more useful for larger integers or for non-integers.

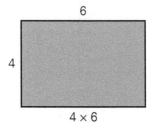

The area model can be partitioned to break down larger numbers, creating a grid. In this example, we see how 16×13 is broken, through distributivity, into $10 \times 10 + 10 \times 6 + 3 \times 10 + 3 \times 6$. Take a moment to perform this multiplication using a column algorithm and compare what you write to the image below.

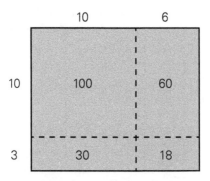

The area model can also be used with algebraic expressions, in a minimal extension of its use with numbers. Used alongside algebra tiles (see below), this is a powerful representation of multiplication with expressions.

	$2x$	4
$3x$	$6x^2$	$12x$
6	$12x$	24

Place value tables

Place value tables are another commonly used and important representation. It is used throughout primary school and into secondary school to help pupils make sense of numerals, understanding that each digit in a numeral represents a different value depending on its place. A place value table therefore helps to expose the structure of our number system.

The column headings can be expressed in words, using fractions (to the right of the decimal point) and powers of ten. These can be combined to show their equivalence.

Hundreds	Tens	Ones	Tenths	Hundredths	Thousandths
100	10	1	$\frac{1}{10}$	$\frac{1}{100}$	$\frac{1}{1000}$
10^2	10^1	10^0	10^{-1}	10^{-2}	10^{-3}

The place value table can be used alongside concrete manipulatives that represent base ten, such as place value counters and Dienes blocks. Take care using blocks or counters and the place value table together. If placed inside the table, two ten blocks in the tens column could be seen to represent 20 lots of ten, not 2 lots of 10.

The place value table can be used to compare the relative size of numbers, to model column addition with whole numbers and decimals, especially the 'exchange' of something like 10 ones for 1 ten and it provides an excellent representation when multiplying or dividing by powers of ten and when introducing standard form.

Bar model

A bar model is used to represent quantities, known and unknown, and the relationship between them. It represents the structure of a problem to reveal the process that should be used. Take this question, for example.

Jim is carrying 7 books and Anne is carrying 15 books. Anne gives Jim some books so that they are each carrying the same number of books. How many books does Anne give Jim?

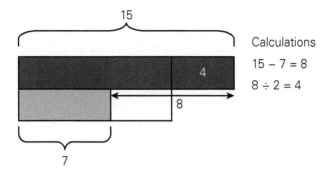

Calculations

$15 - 7 = 8$

$8 \div 2 = 4$

A bar model bridges the gap between concrete mathematical experiences and abstract representations. This begins in primary school when concrete objects are arranged in a line and counted. For instance:

Andy has 3 apples and Blossom has 2 apples. How many apples do they have altogether?

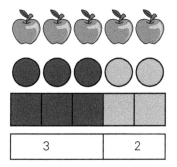

$3 + 2 = 5$

A bar model can represent key concepts such as addition, subtraction, multiplication, division, ratio, proportion and percentages. In the example above, we can see that the ratio of Andy's apples to Blossom's is 3:2 and that Andy has $1\frac{1}{2}$ times as many apples as Blossom, and that Blossom has $\frac{2}{3}$ as many as Andy. As questions become more complex, a bar model can demonstrate the idea of a variable and can model solving linear equations and simultaneous equations. They build nicely on the concrete manipulative of Cuisenaire rods.

Bar models do not easily represent positive and negative numbers at the same time, but can be used in conjunction with a number line. The following diagram compares +3 with −7.

Commonly-used concrete representations

Cuisenaire rods

These are a set of ten coloured rods invented by Georges Cuisenaire and popularised by Caleb Gattegno in the 1950s. The rods are each 1 cm wide and range in length from 1 cm to 10 cm. Each rod does not have an assigned numerical value – any rod can be considered the 'unit'.

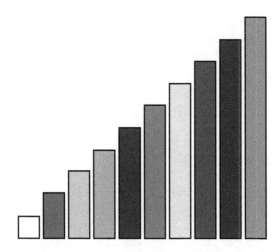

Cuisenaire rods can be formed into trains, which makes their connection with bar modelling clear. They can also be used at right angles to create area models.

Cuisenaire rods can be used to explore a wide range of mathematical ideas including cardinality, number bonds, equality, equivalence, algebraic expressions, factors and primes, and for modelling additive and multiplicative relationships as well as fractions and decimals.

Counters

Counters are the most readily available and versatile manipulative in most classrooms. They provide a concrete item for counting. They can be arranged into arrays to show multiplication, division, factorisation and prime numbers. They can be used to demonstrate the commutative law and the distributive law, and offer ways of thinking about the four operations as well as demonstrating equivalent ratios.

Two coloured counters are usually yellow on one side to represent +1 and red on the other side to represent −1, meaning they can represent addition, subtraction, multiplication and division with directed numbers. One key idea used in this model is that of the *zero pair* – the result of a negative counter being added to a positive counter. Another key idea is that multiplication by a negative is modelled by flipping a counter over.

$$-3 + 2 = -1$$

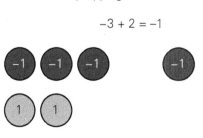

Base ten blocks

Dienes blocks, named after Zoltan Dienes, consist of a small cube, 10 small cubes arranged in a line, 100 small cubes arranged in a square and 1000 small cubes arranged in a large cube. These represent the ones, tens, hundreds and thousands of our decimal system. They can be extended to represent decimals by calling the large cube 1, making the square $\frac{1}{10}$, the line $\frac{1}{100}$ and the small cube $\frac{1}{1000}$.

This manipulative reveals the structure of the decimal system, the idea that each column in the place value chart is ten times smaller than the one to its left. One of the key ideas is that of *exchange*: you can exchange 10 ones for 1 ten, for example.

Dienes blocks are useful to expose the process of addition when using the column method and when used alongside the standard algorithm. The same is true for subtraction, multiplication and division.

Another use for the Dienes block is when working on length, area and volume, particularly when calculating with different units of measure. They also reveal the link between powers of 1, 2 and 3 and one, two and three dimensions.

Place value counters

Place value counters can be used in similar ways to Dienes blocks to reveal the structure of our decimal number system. While they don't communicate the relative size of digits, they help once that aspect of understanding is in place.

2132

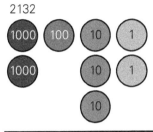

100 000	10 000	1 000	100	10	1
		2	1	3	2

Algebra tiles

A set of algebra tiles contains a small yellow square tile which has side length 1 and therefore an area of 1 square unit, a green rectangular tile with lengths of 1 and x and therefore an area of x, and a large blue square tile with side length x and an area of x^2.

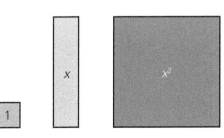

Well-made algebra tiles will have an x dimension that is not a multiple of 1 making it less likely that pupils assign a value to x based on how many 1s fit along its side.

Each algebra tile is coloured red on its reverse side to represent -1, $-x$ and $-x^2$.

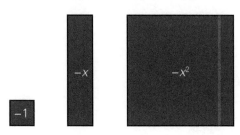

In the same way as double-sided counters, the small '1' tile can be used to represent directed numbers. The shape of the tiles allows them to be arranged into a continuous area model, and can be used to show representation of addition, subtraction, multiplication and division. The use of these tiles provides a clear mental model of the nature of these processes.

When the x tile is introduced, the same processes used with the '1' tile can be used to simplify expressions by collecting like terms. We use the area model to represent expanding and factorising with single and double brackets.

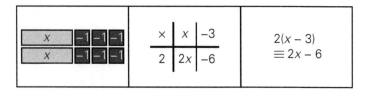

The manipulation of the algebra tiles is used alongside pictorial and symbolic representations to help pupils confidently move towards the symbolic at a pace appropriate to them. The algebra tiles can be used to represent the processes involved with expanding and factorising quadratics and completing the square, giving a coherent model that works from elementary number through to some of the highest-level algebra on the compulsory school curriculum.

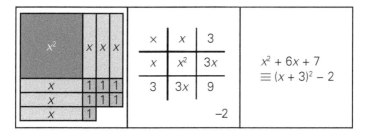

Like all manipulatives, algebra tiles have their limitations: the idea of a negative area can be problematic (although not insurmountable – see Mark McCourt's *Teaching for Mastery* for an explanation of how to work with negative areas) and they cannot model any expression of greater dimension than a quadratic. However, they are excellent at communicating mathematical concepts of addition and multiplication with variables, and laying the ground for symbolic notation to take over eventually.

Multiple representations

Abstract mathematical concepts can only be thought about, discussed, taught and learnt through representations. As James Kaput (1987) said, 'representation and symbolization are ... at the heart of cognitions associated with mathematical activity'. Most of us start teaching with confidence in the symbolic representations of numerals and letters, but by widening the range of representations we use, we can expose more of the properties of a concept and enable pupils to make meaning. The use of multiple representations is therefore a powerful thing in teaching mathematics.

Let's take fractions, for instance. We represent the idea of 'two wholes split into five equal parts' (or 'two out of five equal parts') with the language 'two fifths', and the symbolic notation $\frac{2}{5}$.

We could also use a concrete manipulative such as Cuisenaire rods:

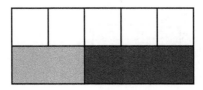

Or an image such as a fraction wall:

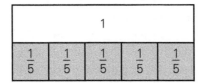

We must show it on a number line at some point to communicate that, not only is a fraction a way of splitting up a whole, but it is also a number in its own right, with a decimal equivalent:

Each of these representations is useful to emphasise a certain aspect of fractions and deepens conceptual understanding. If we used just one or two of these representations, it would be harder for pupils to make all the connections they should.

Getting started with concrete and pictorial representations

It is a good idea to work collaboratively with colleagues when developing ideas in our teaching, as we discussed in Chapters 1 and 2. Discussing the merits and flaws of any approach deepens our understanding and encourages us to give it a go. Having shared approaches between colleagues will provide for consistency in pupils' learning experiences and prevents confusion when a pupil changes class.

If you are very new to thinking about representations, you might want to start with a more familiar idea such as the number line. Discuss with your colleagues where this could be used throughout your curriculum, so that its regularity of use breeds familiarity. Ask yourselves questions about its use – how could you model addition/directed numbers, etc.? Check accessibility – are there number lines already visible in classrooms? Check whether or not they were used regularly in primary school; if so, pupils already have a strong knowledge of them. If they were, how? It is useful to know how learning develops both before and after the phase you are teaching.

Take it slowly; do not introduce all the different representations in this chapter at once. Choose a couple to focus on. Remember that we do not want to introduce an unfamiliar model with a new mathematical idea as this will lead to cognitive overload. It is better to introduce a representation with mathematics that your pupils are already comfortable with. Then, when the pupils are comfortable with the representation, introduce the new mathematical idea using it. A representation isn't something for the pupils to learn in itself, but it must be familiar to them so that it can be used as a way to develop their understanding of the underlying concepts. Models and manipulatives should not become another procedure that the pupils must recall – we should sooner find ourselves saying, *'Let's see what this problem would look like if we used a bar model,'* rather than, *'Today we are learning bar modelling.'*

We should not separate the use of concrete manipulatives or pictorial representations from symbolic notation. These representations are used as different ways of seeing the mathematics in order to make meaning, and to help pupils move towards the symbolic in a robust way. They should never be used as crutches for lower-attaining pupils or referred to as something only younger pupils use, as doing so might communicate that they are not valuable for higher attainers or older pupils, which is simply not true. We can all use different representations to explore the same ideas and deepen our understanding.

Before introducing representations to a class, make sure you are comfortable with the model or manipulative you intend to use. Allow yourself plenty of time to get to know the concrete manipulatives, such as algebra tiles or Cuisenaire rods. Practise using bar models to model ratio problems. Start by just playing with them and then think about what they show us. There is a wealth of information available to guide you through the different representations, both on websites such as the NCETM www.ncetm.org.uk and in books such a Peter Mattock's *Visible Mathematics*.

Recognise that there are flaws and limitations to the representations we use. There are cases where trying to model a question using a bar model, for instance, is harder than using symbolic notation, for example when solving linear equations with negatives such as

$$2a + 10 = 4$$

This does not negate the use of a bar model in many other cases; it simply highlights what we knew from the start of this chapter, that the symbolic notation is the most transferable (and, for many pupils, the hardest to get your head around). Remember, each representation is just one way to make sense of a concept while developing fluency.

Prepare yourself well before introducing manipulatives with a class. Make sure your classroom routines are well established and you are clear about all instructions. Think about what could go wrong. Will the pupils be messing about with the manipulatives while you need their attention? The ideas explored in Chapter 2 will help with this. One thing to say on on practical level, is that you should not avoid using manipulatives with 'difficult' classes. *'I'm not using algebra tiles with 8T – they will just throw them at each other!'* It is far better to deal with the behavioural issues using every trick in the book (even if it means drafting in extra help from the senior leadership team (SLT) or head of department (HOD)), than to deny pupils the opportunity to develop their understanding. You might even find that using a practical resource helps.

If you do not have access to physical manipulatives, there are digital versions on websites such as Mathsbot (www.mathsbot.com). They can also be used to explore ideas, even if your class are not using the physical manipulatives.

Language, questioning and discussion are all important when working with representations. In order for pupils to make meaning when using multiple representations, they will need to be actively encouraged to make connections between the concrete, pictorial and symbolic representations. If you are new to using multiple representations, it is a good idea to script the lesson beforehand to make sure you are clear on how each action with the physical manipulative links with each step in the symbolic procedure. You are unlikely to follow this script, but it will clarify your thoughts in readiness for the lesson.

Implementation of manipulatives

We spoke to Mike Marrison, the head of mathematics at Flegg High Ormiston Academy, to find out about the department's journey with implementation of manipulatives.

The maths department at Flegg High were bringing in a new curriculum, OAT Mathematics, starting with Year 7. Although most staff had knowledge of the CPA approach and drew pictorial representations in their practice, using the physical manipulatives described in the curriculum was new to most. They hoped that the approach would allow more pupils to access the curriculum and help pupils to make connections. There were some dusty manipulatives in the department, such as Numicon and Cuisenaire rods, but they were never used.

The team began exploring and developing their knowledge of manipulatives and how they are used. After thinking about where they could be most beneficial, they decided to focus on algebra and directed number so bought algebra tiles and two-colour counters. Their regional lead practitioner led training sessions that allowed staff to get to know the manipulatives and how best to use them in the classroom. There was also training from the MathsHub and the head of department shared his knowledge, experience and learning from personal CPD.

There are always challenges when implementing something new to both staff and pupils. Teachers felt that the manipulatives were very successful with the younger pupils that were being introduced to topics for the first time. They trusted and engaged with the use of manipulatives and showed deeper understanding as a consequence. It was more difficult to introduce the manipulatives with groups that had pre-existing knowledge of the topics, as they tended to revert to using familiar methods without making connections with the manipulatives.

The team has really bought in to this way of working and staff are keen to continue developing the use of manipulatives in their practice, especially with those pupils who are reluctant but would benefit most. When they are working with any new manipulatives in future, they would like to spend more time practising with colleagues in department time before introducing them to the class. The team are working to embed the use of manipulatives in the curriculum to ensure consistency across the department and making use of department time to help with this.

Using representations in a thread through the curriculum

In Chapter 1, we discussed using storytelling as a metaphor for curriculum and planning. In this metaphor, we can see representations as settings in the story. This setting is like a thread that weaves through the curriculum (which we will discuss further in Chapter 9). When a representation is used in this way, it grows in familiarity to the pupils, and they are able to focus on the new learning rather than the representations and make connections to previous learning. As in many stories, the representation itself can develop over time as pupils become secure in some aspects of the concept they are exploring. An example of this is the development of the humble number line.

A curricular thread: number lines

From the start of school, children use a number line to identify and represent numbers. They might use it when counting up in multiples of twos and fives. This is developed throughout primary school to think about multiplication as repeated addition.

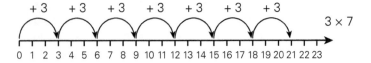

Around the time pupils come to secondary school, multiplication may be thought about as stretching or scaling. Again, this can be modelled on a number line.

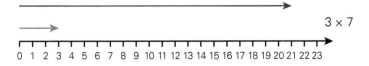

The number line, with vectors, can be used to communicate addition and subtraction with directed numbers.

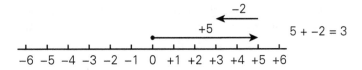

If we take two orthogonal number lines, we have a Cartesian graph:

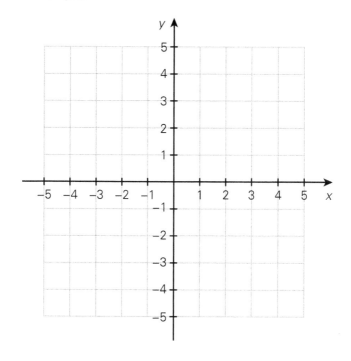

Combined with vectors, we can explore addition and subtraction in two dimensions:

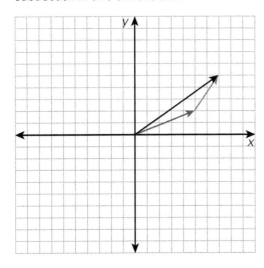

$$\begin{pmatrix} 5 \\ 2 \end{pmatrix} + \begin{pmatrix} 2 \\ 3 \end{pmatrix} = \begin{pmatrix} 7 \\ 5 \end{pmatrix}$$

When pupils start thinking about proportional relationships, two number lines can be stacked on top of each other, with the zeros lined up. These double number lines can be used whenever we are exploring the multiplicative relationship between two quantities.

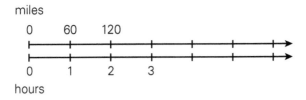

Once this has become a firm mental model, the ratio table can be introduced. The ratio table can be seen as a reduction of the double number line, without the scale.

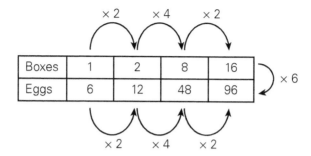

Once we move onto teaching proportional formulae of the form $y = kx$, we can see the constant of proportionality in the double number line or ratio table.

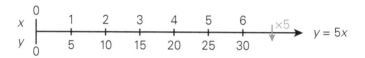

And from then on, any proportional relationship can be shown through this representation.

x^2	1	4	9	16
y	2	8	18	32

$\big)$ × 2 $y = 2x^2$

$\frac{1}{x}$	1	$\frac{1}{2}$	$\frac{1}{4}$	$\frac{1}{8}$
y	24	12	6	3

$\big)$ × 24 $y = \frac{24}{x}$

The number line, itself developed over time, provides a structural model that connects topics as superficially diverse as long division, direct proportion and pie charts, revealing that, underneath their appearance, they are not that different after all.

Chapter Summary

This chapter explores some of the ways we can represent school mathematics. It has given an introduction to some of the commonly used models and manipulatives and why we use a concrete, pictorial and symbolic approach.

- Conceptual understanding should be developed alongside procedural fluency.
- We must represent maths in some way in order to communicate it.
- The use of physical manipulatives or pictorial representations should not be viewed as support for younger pupils or low attainers.
- Using multiple representations can reveal different aspects of a concept and deepen understanding.
- Representations can be used to make links between seemingly unconnected topics.
- Collaborate with colleagues and spend time getting to know models and manipulatives, before introducing them to your classes.

FURTHER READING

Visible Maths – Peter Mattock (2019). This excellent book provides descriptions of key representations, how they can be used to model different areas of mathematics, as well as their limitations.

Teaching for Mastery – Mark McCourt (2019). This book contains clear and detailed discussions of how Cuisenaire rods and algebra tiles can be woven throughout a curriculum to expose mathematical concepts.

In *Toward a Theory of Instruction* (1966) Jerome Bruner sets out the ideas around representation that subsequent generations have built upon.

Helen Drury's *Mastering Mathematics* (2014) is a thorough discussion of how to develop mathematical proficiency.

Why Don't Children Like School by Daniel Willingham (2021) sets out a strong case for framing instruction against a backdrop of cognitive psychology.

5

Reasoning and problem-solving

Mathematical knowledge can be categorised in different ways. One way is to split it into 'substantive' and 'disciplinary' knowledge. Substantive knowledge is the substance of the subject, the procedures and concepts that pupils study every lesson. Every chapter so far has been focused on how we can help as many pupils as possible to learn this kind of knowledge.

Disciplinary knowledge is different. This is the knowledge of how mathematics is discovered and created, how it is used by mathematicians and others involved in the discipline of mathematics outside of the classroom. The disciplinary knowledge of mathematics can be elusive and needs careful thought to its development.

We could call the disciplinary knowledge of mathematics 'mathematical thinking' or 'mathematical habits of mind'. In their influential book *Thinking Mathematically*, John Mason, Leone Burton and Kaye Stacey draw on the work of Caleb Gattegno – a prolific mathematics educator of the twentieth century – to teach us that once we become *aware* of how to apply mathematics to different contexts or problems, we begin to think mathematically. This tells us one component of what it means to think in a mathematical way: having the ability to use the mathematics we have learnt in a novel context.

This kind of activity is different to rehearsing what the teacher has just taught us. It is different from retrieving or recalling things we learnt about in the past. It is internalising mathematical knowledge to the degree that we can apply it when we haven't been primed to do so. We might call this having fluency or flexibility of knowledge, and it is this flexibility that allows us to think and act mathematically.

There are certain behaviours that demonstrate mathematical thinking. These include:

- asking mathematical questions (quantitative, spatial, statistical, probabilistic)

- modelling

- specialising

- generalising

- conjecturing

- visualising

- pattern-seeking

- justifying

- reasoning

- convincing

- proving.

It might be tempting to think that only the highest attainers in our classrooms can think mathematically, or that only pupils at the end of a course can show these behaviours, but this is not the case. Pupils at every stage of their education can display these behaviours using the knowledge that they have at that moment and, importantly, every pupil should be given opportunities to see and practise these behaviours. So, as with everything we teach, mathematical thinking must be carefully developed over time, enabling pupils to reach a state of relative proficiency in it by the end of their time with us. With careful thought and deliberate instruction, we can help every child to think mathematically.

Understanding

Any discussion around developing mathematical thinking should hold in mind the concept of mathematical understanding. What does it mean to *understand* mathematics? To help us consider this question, read this list of statements about someone's proficiency with multiplication and ask yourself: at what stage could it be said that the pupil *understands* multiplication?

1. They know their multiplication tables up to 12 × 12.

2. They can represent numbers in the multiplication tables as an array, such as this one below for 3 × 4:

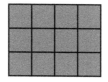

3. They can multiply a two- or three-digit number by a one-digit number using a column method.

4. They can multiply numbers of any size using a column method.

5. They know that division is the inverse of multiplication.

6. They can divide using a written method such as long or short division.

7. They can multiply and divide numbers outside the multiplication tables in their head using distributivity, e.g.

$43 \times 5 = 40 \times 5 + 3 \times 5 = 120 + 15 = 135$, or

$168 \div 8 = 160 \div 8 + 8 \div 8 = 20 + 1 = 21$.

8. They can multiply and divide numbers outside the multiplication tables in their head using associativity, e.g.

$12 \times 25 = 3 \times 4 \times 25 = 3 \times 100 = 300$, or

$198 \div 6 = 198 \div 2 \div 3 = 99 \div 3 = 33$.

9. They can multiply and divide with decimals using written methods.

10. They can multiply and divide with decimals in their head, employing distributivity, associativity, and their knowledge of integers.

11. They can multiply and divide proper and improper fractions and mixed numbers.

12. They know that multiplication increases dimensions and is used to calculate areas and volumes.

13. They can represent multiplication as a scale of a vector on a number line, such as this one for 3×4:

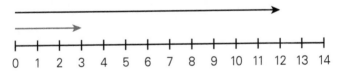

14. They can use multiplicative reasoning and the idea of scaling to answer questions of proportionality.

15. They know that multiplication with numbers can be generalised using algebraic expressions.

16. They can perform multiplication procedures on linear expressions, such as:

$$2(x + 1) = 2x + 2 \text{ or } 3x - 6 = 3(x - 2).$$

17. They can perform multiplication procedures on quadratic expressions, such as:

$$(x + 5)(x - 2) = x^2 + 3x - 10 \text{ or}$$
$$2x^2 + 7x + 6 = (2x + 3)(x + 2).$$

18. They can represent algebraic multiplication as an area model, such as this one below for $x^2 + 2x + 1$:

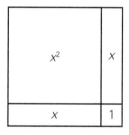

We could write more, but we will stop there. Where did you draw the line? Where did you say, 'Now they understand multiplication'? Did you struggle to draw such a line?

Hopefully it is clear that there is no such line. There is no point where you can say, 'Now I understand multiplication.' What happens is more like connecting a web. You learn things that can be grouped under the title 'Multiplication' but then you connect them to other ideas and concepts. Understanding can be thought of as an increasingly complex web of concepts and procedures you know about and the connections between them. This web is called a 'schema'. The more complex the schema, the greater (or deeper) the understanding.

When we first learn something, our knowledge can be said to be *inflexible*. We can perhaps mimic the teacher and reproduce a fact or process. Over time, with the right practice, we can apply our knowledge correctly with less conscious effort, we can link it with other bits of knowledge and to invoke it in unfamiliar, or novel, contexts. This is when knowledge becomes more flexible.

The challenge for the teacher, then, is what makes the right kind of practice, the kind of practice that allows a pupil to gain flexibility of knowledge. Much of what we talk about in Chapter 4 on representations and Chapter 9 on curriculum explores this, and there are whole books dedicated to great mathematical tasks (see *Further Reading*). Here we will focus on the role of reasoning, problem-solving and inquiry in developing flexible knowledge and mathematical thinking, but first we must consider 'basic' practice.

Varied practice

Not all practice is created alike. We should think about how the practice pupils get pushes their boundaries of understanding. Sticking with multiplication, and imagining that we are teaching pupils about expanding and factorising with a single bracket, a typical moment of teacher instruction might look like this:

Teacher: *To expand a bracket we multiply everything outside the bracket by everything inside the bracket. Here is an example:*

$$2(x+5) = 2x+10$$

We multiply x by 2 and positive 5 by 2, giving us $2x+10$. Now you try this one. [Gives the pupils a similar example.]

The pupils mimic the procedure and the teacher will give them practice questions. Take a look at the questions in the table.

More standard practice	Less standard practice
$4(x + 3)$	$4(3 - x)$
$4(2x + 3)$	$-4(x - 3)$
$4(2x - 3)$	$-4(3 - x)$
$x(x + 3)$	$\dfrac{1}{4}(x + 3)$
	$\dfrac{x + 3}{4}$
	$-(x - 3)$

A sequence of questions such as those on the left will allow pupils some familiarity with the process. For building flexibility, however, they are insufficient. Pupils' flexibility with the process is more likely to improve if, at some point, they work on questions like those on the right, which bring in calculations with negatives, make the link between multiplication and division, and use non-standard presentations.

To build connections, we should explicitly link the process of expanding a bracket to the process of multiplication with numbers. We saw in Chapter 4 that consistent representations help pupils to make links. In this case, if multiplication with numbers has been taught using a grid and area model, then using the same representations for multiplication with expressions will help connect the new learning to the old.

×	10	3
10	100	30
4	40	12

×	x	3
x	x^2	$3x$
4	$4x$	12

The way we teach and the practice we give our pupils can increase flexibility of knowledge. Once this happens, we must give pupils opportunities to use this knowledge in increasingly complex and varied ways, including through reasoning.

Reasoning

The OED defines 'to reason' as '*to think in a connected or logical manner; to employ the faculty of reason in forming conclusions*'. Reasoning is being able to use knowledge to make justifications or explanations; to generalise, to find relationships and to prove them. To understand what this looks like in the mathematics classroom, we could start by imagining the endpoint: what a pupil can do if we consider them good at reasoning. We might say that to be good at reasoning is to be able to:

- explain how a process works
- justify why each stage of a process is valid
- explain why someone else's solution is incorrect and put it right

- prove a mathematical statement

- find patterns, commonalities and differences

- generalise from patterns or examples.

This is not an exhaustive list but does include some of the most common evidence of an ability to reason mathematically.

To be able to reason, we must have opportunity to think in this way, so we must see questions that prompt this kind of thinking and be taught how to approach them. Questions that prompt us to reason can take many forms. Here are some examples; before reading on, take a moment to have a go at them.

1. What happens to the digits in a number when you multiply it by 10, 100, 1000?

2. *'A number with five hundreds will always be greater than a number with two hundreds.'*

    Is this statement correct? Explain your reasoning.

3. *'Division always makes a number smaller.'* Is this statement correct? Explain your reasoning.

4. Put these quadrilaterals into groups according to their features: rhombus, square, rectangle, trapezium, kite, arrowhead, parallelogram.

5. Prove that the sum of three consecutive integers is always divisible by three.

6. Pupil A says, *'Exactly $\frac{2}{7}$ of the pupils in the class wear glasses.'* In Pupil A's class there are 30 pupils. Explain how you know they must be wrong.

7. The sides of a triangle are labelled as 5 cm, 12 cm and 14 cm. Can the triangle be right-angled? Explain how you know.

8. Every possible quadratic graph can be obtained by transforming the graph of $y = x^2$. Explain how this can be true.

How easy did you find each question? Did the answers appear to you with little thought or did you have to ponder them for a while? Compare those you found easier with those you found harder: where do you think the difference lies?

It is likely that the ones you found easier are the ones where your knowledge of the underlying mathematics is stronger – where you feel more confident. This is because reasoning is not a generic skill that can be thought of in isolation. We reason *about* something. We can't say, '*I can reason*', but we *can* say, '*I can reason about linear equations*,' and we can say that, because our underlying knowledge of linear equations is fluent and flexible enough to allow us to think in a logical way about them, to make sense of the processes involved and explain why they work as they do.

Let us explore this in some more detail. Take this question and (incorrect) solution:

Solve the equation $6x + 7 = 9$.

$$6x + 7 = 9$$
$$6x = 2$$
$$x = 3$$

A pupil who is good at reasoning about linear equations might be able to explain that we start by subtracting 7 from both sides, rather than divide by 6, maybe with some reference to the reverse order of operations. They might also be able to explain why we perform the inverse of the operations we see in the equation, perhaps talking about *'undoing'*. They might spot that the answer should be $\frac{2}{6}$, not $\frac{6}{2}$, saying something about, *'dividing by the coefficient of* ***x****'*. If they could explain the last stage with a visual, or talk about sharing 2 into 6 parts to determine x, or talk about dividing by 6 being the inverse of multiplying by 6, then we could say that they are able to reason through the equation, but hopefully it is becoming clear that reasoning exists on some kind of spectrum. The ability to reason about linear equations will become better as understanding of all the component parts increases – in other words, as flexibility increases.

This can be a puzzle for a maths teacher: how do I help my pupils to practise procedures, to make connections and to practise reasoning and mathematical thinking so that, over time, they become better at all three? The answer – as tends to be the way with teaching – is not formulaic, and will probably vary between pupils, but there are general principles we can use to guide us.

Go back to the eight sample reasoning questions. There were probably some you had to think about more than others. This cognitive effort is a good thing if used at the right time. Too early in the learning process and it will likely overwhelm pupils and contribute to a feeling that mathematics is too hard. As they become more expert, the amount they will learn from such a question reduces. The challenge is to pose questions at the time when pupils will be able to think about them properly, when they have a decent chance of success, but when they still have something to learn by completing the question. Identifying the right time is not an exact science, but there are two prompts you can ask yourself to help:

- Is the pupil relatively adept at the underlying mathematics?

- Does the pupil need stretching further to gain a better understanding of the concept?

Let's think about question 7 in the light of these prompts:

The sides of a triangle are labelled as 5 cm, 12 cm and 14 cm. Can the triangle be right-angled? Explain how you know.

Answering the question requires Pythagoras' Theorem. If a pupil can confidently answer standard Pythagoras' Theorem questions, and perhaps some less standard ones, and they know that the theorem can only be used when a triangle is right-angled, then a question such as this one could be just right to deepen their understanding, drawing their attention to the converse of the theorem: that if $a^2 + b^2 \neq c^2$ then the triangle cannot be right-angled.

Posing reasoning questions at the right time is part of the art of teaching mathematics. Done well, we achieve two aims: we help to deepen pupils' understanding and we help pupils to learn to communicate mathematically. Developing mathematical communication should be seen as a long-term process, much like the development of mathematical knowledge itself.

Pupils come to us from primary school not only with different starting points in their knowledge but also with different starting points in their ability to communicate that knowledge. Some will be confident when speaking, some when writing, some both, some neither. We must use our time with them to develop their mathematical communication and this is where our approach to reasoning questions can be very powerful. Simply posing a question might be sufficient for those pupils who are already strong in communicating mathematics. For many pupils, however, the question alone is not enough. In these cases, the way we use it in the classroom can be pivotal.

Scaffolding the communication process allows pupils to learn not only to reason, but to explain their reasoning well.

Imagine a pupil who is ready to tackle question 7, the Pythagoras' Theorem question, but who struggles to explain what they are thinking and gives an answer like this:

Pupil: *It's not, because the numbers don't work.*

You know what they mean, you know they understand what they're doing, but their communication was not strong. If you reword the answer for them and move on, they have lost an opportunity to practise and improve their communication. Such a pupil might benefit from one of the scaffolds in the table below.

Scaffold	Example	How it works
Sentence stems	Teacher provides the start of a sentence to answer the question: *The triangle <u>can/cannot</u> be right-angled because $6^2 + 12^2$ equals _____, and...*	Demonstrating the use of (part of) a full sentence, the pupil is then asked to use it to say their answer again.
Key words on board	Teacher writes useful mathematical words, such as *'Pythagoras' Theorem'*, *'square'* and *'hypotenuse'* on the board, then asks the pupil to explain again using those words.	Reminds pupils of the relevant mathematical vocabulary and requires them to select the right word at the right time.

Scaffold	Example	How it works
Peer review	The teacher asks pairs of pupils to explain to each other and to improve each other's explanation.	When pupils need to rehearse and refine an explanation without all eyes on them, doing so with a partner before coming back to the whole class can be useful.
Repetition or choral response	The teacher gives a clear explanation and asks pupils to repeat out loud.	Allows pupils to practise words and sentences out loud as a group, without all eyes on them.

As time goes on, with sufficient classroom practice at communication, pupils will find it easier to explain their reasoning in a coherent and mathematical way. Developing this alongside developing mathematical knowledge is important.

Problem-solving

The mathematician Paul Halmos, writing in 1980, told us that solving problems is 'the heart of mathematics'. He explains how solving problems is the dominant activity of mathematicians, who discover or pose problems as part of their work and use known mathematics, or create new mathematics, to solve them. We can think of problem-solving as part of the disciplinary knowledge of mathematics along with much of the activity mentioned in the earlier discussion of reasoning: conjecture, proof, justification, generalisation, and so on.

One of the three main aims of the English National Curriculum is that all pupils 'can solve problems by applying their mathematics to a variety of routine and non-routine problems with increasing sophistication, including breaking down problems into a series of simpler steps and persevering in seeking solutions' (DfE, 2021). The American Common Core sets its first Standard for Mathematical Practice as, 'Make sense of problems and persevere in solving them.' (2022, p. 6) In Singapore, the Mathematics Curriculum Framework (Ministry of Education Singapore, 2012) places problem-solving at the centre emphasising a belief that it is the heart of mathematical endeavour.

In fact, most jurisdictions worldwide prize problem-solving in their mathematics curricula, and rightly so, because the ability to solve mathematical problems is a strong indicator that a pupil has flexible knowledge. Despite this, there remains a lack of clarity about how to integrate problem-solving into a curriculum and how to teach pupils to solve problems well.

Some people advocate teaching mathematics *through* problem-solving, whereby solving problems is the primary medium for bringing pupils to new mathematical knowledge. Indeed, this is an established pedagogical practice in Japan and the focus of a 2021 book by Japanese educator Akihiko Takahashi (2021). Takahashi describes how teachers pose problems as a way of introducing new mathematical concepts, observing what happens and leading whole-class discussion of approaches in order to draw pupils to the new knowledge. We will look at this approach a little more in our discussion of inquiry at the end of the chapter.

Others argue that it is possible to teach *about* problem-solving. George Pólya, a Hungarian mathematician, wrote the influential book *How to Solve It* in 1945, where he sets out a four-step process for solving problems, which pupils can use to their benefit:

1. First, you have to understand the problem.

2. After understanding, make a plan.

3. Carry out the plan.

4. Look back on your work. How could it be better?

Pólya suggests questions to help understand the problem, including, 'Can you restate the problem in your own words?' and 'Can you think of a picture or diagram that might help you understand the problem?'. To make a plan, he suggests strategies, or heuristics, including looking for patterns, using models, working backwards, using a formula, solving a simpler problem, and many more. These ideas have been used in problem-solving curricula (including those in Japan referenced above) and form the basis of approaches to teaching problem-solving advocated by organisations such as NRICH at the University of Cambridge. On the NRICH website you can find problems grouped by strategy rather than by mathematical content. This means you can focus on a strategy such as 'Draw a table' and look at problems that all use that particular strategy (Woodham, 2021).

While the heuristics can be useful, Pólya's four main steps are too vague for someone who is struggling to solve a problem. If you do not understand it, an instruction to 'understand the problem' is not helpful. If you do not know where to start, 'make a plan' gives you no guidance. It is better to read the steps as a *post hoc* analysis of the successful problem-solving process, rather than guidance to give to those who need it.

With a counterargument to the ideas of teaching *about* problem-solving and teaching *through* problem-solving, Sweller, Clark and Kirschner (2010) use research about the role of memory in problem-solving to argue that problem-solving is not a generic skill that can be taught, rather a domain-specific skill that arises as knowledge becomes fluent and flexible. They argue that teaching through problem-solving is inefficient and leads to fewer learning gains than teaching more directly, contrasting the approach with teaching using worked examples. This argument does not, however, negate the use of problems in school mathematics, rather it tells us that we should be conscious of when, why and how we use problems in the classroom.

If you are engaging in a mathematical task that is unfamiliar to you, where you do not immediately know how to reach an answer, or where you could think of various possible approaches without being certain as to which will work, then this task could be classed as a problem. It follows that what constitutes a problem to one person will not to another. A primary age pupil may find the following a problem.

Question 1

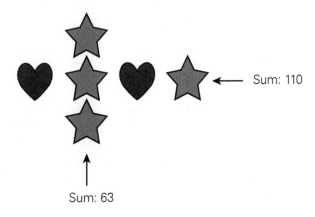

A secondary age pupil may find this trivial, but struggle with something like this.

Question 2

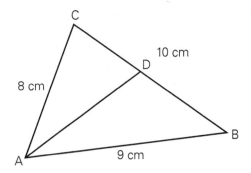

The line AD bisects the angle CAB.
Find the length of the line segment CD.

A university mathematician may find that one trivial, but find themselves grappling with something like this example from Halmos et al. (1975):

Question 3

Is there a non-decreasing continuous function that maps the unit interval into the unit interval so that the length of its graph is equal to 2?

What makes something a problem (or not) is intrinsically linked to the knowledge of the solver: the greater their fluency in the requisite underlying knowledge, the less of a problem the question will be. To the university pupil, only question 3 above will be a problem. To the secondary pupil, both questions 2 and 3 will be problems. To the primary pupil, all three questions will be problems. The important distinction to make, therefore, is which problems could be tackled by each person. We might call this the *accessibility* of the problem. Question 1 is accessible to the primary pupil, but they lack anything close to the requisite knowledge to think about questions 2 and 3, rendering these inaccessible. A problem becomes accessible once the underlying knowledge is in place and becomes trivial (and therefore not a problem) when the solver's knowledge has far surpassed that required in the question.

At this point, we should also make a distinction between *routine* and *non-routine* problems. A routine problem is one which can be solved in similar ways to those already seen, perhaps by following steps or using familiar processes. A non-routine problem is one where '*there is not a predictable, well-rehearsed approach or pathway explicitly suggested by the task, task instructions, or a worked out example*' (Stein and Lane, 1996, p. 58). A problem that is routine to one person will be non-routine to another and, crucially, the routine nature of a problem will depend upon where pupils meet it. For instance, if you are at the end of a sequence of lessons on Pythagoras' Theorem, then a problem that uses Pythagoras' Theorem will be less routine than if you use it a month later after teaching something else.

Problems have an important place in the school curriculum. We have already pointed out that they can be used to demonstrate fluency in the underlying mathematics since they can be accessed and tackled successfully once the requisite knowledge is secure and flexible, but there is another important consideration in the use of problems, which has to do with the expertise-reversal effect.

The expertise-reversal effect refers to the type of instruction that most benefits pupils of different levels of expertise, or prior knowledge. The effect tells us that when a pupil's knowledge is inflexible, when they are first learning and making connections, they benefit most from clear, direct instruction, worked examples and scaffolding. In other words, novices learn best in a high-guidance environment. In contrast, once a pupil's schema is more connected, when their knowledge is more flexible, high levels of guidance can add cognitive load, making it harder to learn. Experts learn best in a low-guidance environment.

One consequence of the expertise-reversal effect is that more expert pupils will learn by solving problems with minimal guidance. In these cases they can use their knowledge and grapple with how to apply it. They can think about strategies that are appropriate to the problem and they don't have the extra cognitive load of struggling with the underlying mathematics.

This suggests that we can use non-routine problems not just as an indicator of fluency, but as a tool to increase flexibility of knowledge. Just like with reasoning, we can set some rough guidelines to consider when giving pupils problems to solve. If the requisite mathematical knowledge is not in place, the problem is inaccessible and unlikely to help learning. If the requisite knowledge is in place and gaining flexibility, the problem is accessible and likely to help learning. If the requisite knowledge is flexible, fluent and secure, and the problem can be solved with minimum effort, the problem is no longer a problem and unlikely to help learning but could be used as a means of judging a pupil's flexibility of knowledge.

As with our discussion on reasoning earlier in the chapter, our job as teachers is to use the right problem at the right time so that the problem helps pupils to build connections between concepts, or exposes them to more applications of the mathematics, building their schema.

We have now discussed teaching *through* problem-solving, teaching *about* problem-solving and using problems to both improve and assess flexibility of knowledge. There is one more aspect of problem-solving that we should consider: teaching *for* problem-solving. There are activities we can do in the classroom to actively help pupils to get better at solving problems. One of those with the greatest evidence base is teaching pupils to monitor the problem-solving process and reflect on it afterwards, a form of metacognition (Woodward et al., 2012). We can do this in several ways:

- Give pupils a list of reflection prompts or questions and model their use during the process and after. Questions such as, *'How is this problem similar to …?'* or, *'What information might be relevant?'* or *'Does the solution make sense?'* help pupils to think about what they (or others) did, take stock and assess what worked or what could be done better next time.

- Model your thinking process as you solve a problem. This means not simply showing the pupils how to do it but talking them through what you were thinking at each stage.

● Use questioning to interrogate pupils' thinking so that you make explicit to them things they may have done implicitly.

Another powerful tool for improving problem-solving skills is teaching pupils to use visual representations. In Chapter 4 we discussed the importance of visual representations in making the abstract more accessible to more pupils. These representations, when used consistently, also give pupils a greater repertoire of tools with which to tackle non-routine problems.

A third activity that can help improve problem-solving ability (albeit with less strong evidence than the first two) is analysing multiple strategies with pupils. If pupils compare their strategies with those of their peers and, guided by the teacher, analyse the strengths and weaknesses of different strategies, they are likely to get better at selecting effective strategies in future.

The heuristics we mentioned for solving problems: visualising or drawing an image, working backwards, trial and improvement, testing individual numbers (specialising), looking for patterns, finding a rule (generalising) and working systematically (making tables, for instance) can be learnt by practising problems that use each strategy. Some people advocate working on groups of problems that use the same strategy (rather than the same mathematics) together in a block. However, there is evidence that interleaving problems that use different strategies helps pupils to choose the correct strategy (Van Merriënboer and Kirschner, 2018). If we call our strategies A, B and C, then a blocked approach might look like this: AABBCC where an interleaved approach would look like this: ABACCBAB, with the strategies mixed up. It is thought that interleaving allows pupils to compare and contrast strategies as they are learning which, although more difficult in the short term, leads to greater long-term learning effects.

All of these recommendations come in the context of the earlier discussion: that to be an effective solver of problems, a pupil will need some degree of flexibility in the underlying mathematics. Hugh Burkhardt of the Shell Centre for Mathematical Education in Nottingham, which has been designing instructional materials and researching mathematics education since 1967, talks of a 'few-year gap' between pupils' initial encounters with a mathematical idea and having flexible enough knowledge of it to solve problems reliably (2018). It is this kind of gap (providing pupils have been engaged in meaningful practice in the interim) that allows for fluency in the mathematical knowledge underpinning a problem, making space for the pupil to concentrate on solving the problem itself.

Inquiry

Inquiry is the kind of activity a mathematician engages in when they notice something and try to explain it through the lens of mathematics. Perhaps the most famous inquiry is that of Isaac Newton and the apple. In observing the falling apple, Newton was prompted to ask himself why objects always fall to earth. In considering the question, he was led to the concept of forces and their modelling with mathematics. The falling apple was a *prompt* that led Newton to inquire.

In the classroom, inquiry prompts lead pupils to use the modelling cycle (see below) to set up and solve problems. This is a process with an open beginning, middle and end, which can give pupils the opportunity to use mathematical ways of thinking and mathematical behaviours in a way that is more faithful to the activity of the mathematician.

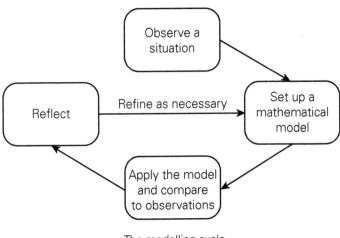

The modelling cycle

An inquiry is set apart from standard problem-solving in that it is likely to be unstructured, with multiple possible answers and no fixed way through to a solution. An inquiry prompt might look like this:

You have to plan a day out for yourself and two friends. You have £100, which must cover food and drink, travel and any other costs. Plan a day that uses as close as possible to the full amount of money, starting no earlier than 8 am and ending no later than 8 pm.

The mathematical activity involved in the inquiry might include reading bus or train timetables, calculating time frames and budgeting, and pupils may have to research possible activities on the internet. In engaging with the inquiry, pupils are required to apply and practise their mathematical knowledge. What is key in the use of inquiry is that pupils ask themselves and each other questions and use the mathematics to answer those questions.

Inquiry prompts can also be used to promote curiosity at the start of a sequence of learning. For instance, if you are starting to teach pupils about fractional indices, you might write this prompt on the board.

$$(49)^{\frac{1}{2}} = 7$$

Ask pupils what they notice. They might see things such as:

- 49 is a square number.

- 7 is the square root of 49.

- There is a fraction in the power, which they have never seen before.

Use what they notice to prompt them to ask questions. Using those questions to explore the statement can lead to uncovering lots of mathematics. Questions might include:

- What might the fraction be telling us to do?

- Can we check our hypothesis with other numbers on the calculator? What would we write?

- How might the fraction look different if we wanted to find a cube root?

By creating curiosity around a prompt, pupils can be motivated to want to know more. By asking questions and engaging in the mathematics required to answer them, pupils are starting to see what it is like to think like a mathematician.

The distinction should be made between inquiry and solving problems, the latter having a pre-determined end point (even if the routes to that point are many), the former being entirely open in its purest form. During inquiry, therefore, the teacher's role takes a particular direction. We must allow pupils to ask questions, to wonder and to notice, but remember that we remain the authority in terms of mathematical knowledge. This means we should not allow discussion to go down useless rabbit holes and should not allow time to be wasted. Most importantly, we should not allow the freedom of discussion to generate misconceptions and misunderstandings. Inquiry can have its place in the classroom, but it is not an efficient way of acquiring new knowledge and, as such, should be used carefully and thoughtfully.

Chapter Summary

As an introduction to problem-solving, reasoning and mathematical thinking and how we can nurture these in the classroom, we have explored some important principles.

- Reasoning is not a generic skill. Rather we reason *about* something we have good knowledge of.
- Giving pupils opportunity to reason mathematically helps them to embed their learning.
- Communicating mathematical reasoning is not always easy and can be scaffolded to help pupils learn to do so.
- Every pupil can access non-routine problems, but they must attempt the right problems at the right time. The right problem is one where the pupil has relative security in the underlying mathematics. The right time is when the pupil still has something to learn, and therefore will benefit from attempting the problem.

There are practices that can be helpful to build problem-solving skills. We should explicitly teach pupils problem-solving strategies.

FURTHER READING

Caleb Gattegno's seminal work, *For the Teaching of Mathematics* (1947–1963).

Thinking Mathematically by John Mason, Leone Burton and Kaye Stacey (2010) explores how to develop mathematical thinking skills.

The *Inquiry Maths* website at www.inquirymaths.com which is full of classroom prompts and how the authors have used them.

For an overview of evidenced strategies to help with problem-solving, read *Improving Mathematical Problem Solving in Grades 4 Through 8* from the What Works Clearinghouse (2018).

6

Enrichment inside and outside the classroom

One of the most demoralising questions an educator can be asked is, *'When will I need to know this in **real** life?'* Perhaps one reason mathematics teachers hear this so frequently is because there is a tendency in society and, to an extent, in schools, to focus on the utility of mathematics, rather than its inherent beauty and value as a discipline. Many mathematics teachers want their pupils to appreciate mathematics for mathematics' sake, but for this to happen we must give them an opportunity to experience the joy and wonder of mathematics rather than simply focusing on what is necessary to pass an exam.

There are multiple ways in which we can enrich pupils' experience of learning mathematics, and enrichment is so much more than just the activities, trips or clubs that take place outside of timetabled mathematics lessons. All pupils deserve to be exposed to mathematical experiences that stretch and intrigue them, not just those pupils already fascinated by or excelling at our subject. The Education Endowment Foundation (n.d.(b)) has stated that *'all children, including those from disadvantaged backgrounds, deserve a well-rounded, culturally rich education'.* Therefore, we need to consider ways in which we can provide a rich education to all pupils in ways which ensure that curriculum time is used effectively.

Hinterland knowledge

In recent years, there has been an increased focus on curriculum in schools in England. Curriculum leaders have spent a large amount of time thinking about how to sequence their curriculum, considering what the core knowledge is for their subject. In mathematics, the National Curriculum is prescriptive, giving little room for choice, so perhaps the area where mathematics teachers have the greatest content decisions to make is that of hinterland knowledge, the knowledge that gives core content more meaning, that supports and feeds it, and broadens pupils' experience.

Christine Counsell (2018) describes curriculum as *'content structured as narrative over time… And every bit of content has a function. That little event early in the novel does a neat job not only in making the early story work, but also of furnishing the reader's memory so that, much later, it resonates in a satisfying resolution or newly puzzling twist.'* Most of the content we teach is core knowledge – that which is essential to know – but some of it is hinterland knowledge, the stuff that increases depth and breadth. Hinterland knowledge is the history of mathematics that piques our curiosity, or the applications that help us to see where the mathematics can take us, or the just-outside-the-curriculum aspects of the mathematics that make us feel that little bit cleverer. Tom Sherrington comments that we cannot be sure what connections can be made by going *'off the beaten track'* with hinterland knowledge but we can be sure that if we do not include any of these forays, our curriculum will be a lot less interesting, a lot more confined and make a whole lot less sense (2019b). In other words, we need the hinterland to truly enrich our curriculum and bring it to life.

To illustrate hinterland knowledge in the mathematics classroom, we will delve into Pythagoras' Theorem. Teaching pupils about Pythagoras' Theorem, we could focus solely on the process of substituting numbers into the formula and solving to find missing sides. However, there are many ways we could add so much more flavour to this topic.

History

It would probably be possible to write a book just about Pythagoras of Samos and his secretive cult of mathematicians. Aside from anything else, many of the stories we can read about him are somewhat conflicting, and there is much dispute over whether some of the more famous tales are actually true. Such stories include:

- Pupils in Pythagoras' school were divided into either *acoustici* (listeners) who could listen to him lecture but had not proven themselves worthy to see him, or *mathematici* who were deemed to be more knowledgeable and could sit behind the curtain where he would give his lectures.

- He drowned one of his pupils either for discovering irrational numbers, or for revealing how to construct a dodecahedron inside a sphere to someone outside of the Pythagorean Brotherhood.

- In spite of this quite bizarre behaviour, Pythagoras was relatively progressive in some ways. Unusually for the time Pythagoras welcomed women to his school (of course, they still had to prove themselves worthy just like the male pupils).

- Pythagoras would not eat beans because he felt they symbolised perfection. The legend goes that this eventually led to his death. An angry mob set fire to the building housing the Pythagorean Brotherhood and although his pupils formed a human bridge allowing Pythagoras to escape, he then came to a field of fava beans. Being unwilling to trample the sacred beans, Pythagoras surrendered to his pursuers.

Even the 'discovery' of the theorem bearing Pythagoras' name is somewhat controversial. A clay tablet has been discovered in Iraq indicating that the Babylonians used the theorem 1000 years before Pythagoras. The ancient Indian mathematician Baudhayana included the theorem in Vedic texts around 300 years before Pythagorean times. There is speculation that Ancient Egyptian surveyors used knotted ropes with sections of length 3, 4 and 5 to assist them in constructing right-angled triangles. There is also evidence that Chinese mathematicians not only knew and used the theorem, but even came up with a proof around the same time as the Pythagoreans, if not slightly earlier, entirely independently of the brotherhood in Greece. Perhaps rather than viewing this information as evidence that Pythagoras was something of a fraud passing off the discoveries of others as his own, we should instead marvel at how mathematical knowledge can be discovered and developed independently in separate places at similar times.

Etymology

When pupils are learning about Pythagoras' Theorem, it is likely to be the first time they come across words like 'theorem' and 'hypotenuse', which can seem a little off-putting and, potentially, quite complicated to say. Explaining a little of the etymology of such words as we go along, as well as being fascinating, can help to begin demystifying them. A little internet search can go a long way here.

- **Theorem** comes from a Greek verb meaning 'to look at, view, behold or consider'; leading to a noun meaning 'a sight, spectacle or thing contemplated by the mind'.

- **Hypotenuse** is also derived from a Greek word, which means 'to stretch under'. It is, in meaning, the same as 'subtend', which we commonly use to describe certain circle theorems. The line is being stretched under or subtended from the right angle.

Visual proofs and demonstrations

There are numerous proofs of the Pythagorean Theorem, some of which are particularly visual (some cite the number of proofs as being over 350 (Brilliant.org, n.d.), but there are broad similarities between many of them). Using a visual proof in the classroom may be pupils' first exposure to the idea of proof, and being able to both *see* the areas we refer to in the theorem, and move them around, allows a potentially tricky concept to really come alive.

The first pair of diagrams show a version of the proof similar to the one used by Pythagoras himself (or at least his brotherhood). By rearranging the four right-angled triangles (demonstrated brilliantly by Eddie Woo at www.youtube.com/watch?v=tTHhBE5lYTg), we can see that $a^2 + b^2 = c^2$.

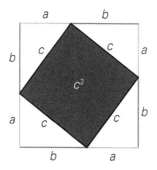
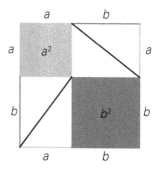

We could also show pupils a Chinese proof, thought to date back to the time of the Zhou Dynasty:

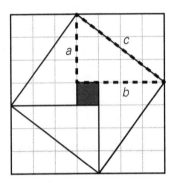

The four right-angled triangles and small square in the centre form an area of c^2

Each triangle has an area of $\dfrac{ab}{2}$

The small, inner square has side length $b - a$ giving an area of $(b - a)^2$

Therefore, $4\dfrac{ab}{2} + (b - a)^2 = c^2$

So $2ab + b^2 - 2ab + a^2 = c^2$

Simplifying to $a^2 + b^2 = c^2$

Probably even more accessible, however, is a water demonstration, which although not a proof can be helpful to create awe and wonder. This can be found in many videos online (such as https://youtu.be/CAkMUdeB06o), where a wheel has been set up with liquid in a container forming the square on the hypotenuse of a right-angled triangle. As the wheel is rotated, the water tips into containers forming the squares on the two legs of the triangle.

Links to other topics

There is a wealth of other mathematical topics where links to Pythagoras' Theorem can be easily made. In some cases, we can include particular question types when pupils are learning about the theorem. In other cases, the opportunities will come later on when learning other topics and finding that Pythagoras' Theorem appears there too. Whenever and however those links are made, the most important thing is to highlight them to the pupils so that they see mathematics as a cohesive whole, rather than a series of disconnected silos. Other areas of mathematics where Pythagoras' Theorem is of use include (but are certainly not limited to):

- circle theorems
- the distance between two co-ordinates
- the equation of a circle
- vectors
- surds
- area and perimeter problems in 2D and 3D.

In particular, an interesting way to link other topics is to consider whether areas of shapes other than squares could be drawn on the sides of a right-angled triangle, so that Area A + Area B = Area C. If you have never seen the following image before, convince yourself why the sum of the two smaller areas must be equal to the larger.

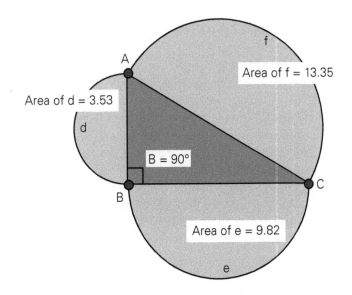

Area of d = 3.53

Area of f = 13.35

B = 90°

Area of e = 9.82

We don't know what we don't know

Pythagoras' Theorem is a particularly rich topic for hinterland knowledge, and it is unlikely that we would have the time to explore everything mentioned above with one class or else we would never actually teach them the whole mathematics curriculum. However, in order to include any of this hinterland knowledge in our teaching, we have to be aware of it ourselves first. There is a wealth of exciting mathematics lurking at the fringes of a multitude of topics but we simply cannot know it all and we don't know what it is that we don't know about! The more we know around the edges of our subject, the more likely that we will be able to make links for our pupils or intrigue and inspire them with snippets of information. Fortunately, there are good ways to explore this hinterland knowledge for ourselves. Although far from an exhaustive list, we have included some good places to start below. Start by taking time to pursue some of the avenues that pique your interest the most and see where it takes you. There will always be something you can share with pupils at a relevant time.

- **Books:** Reading books (like this one!) to help us develop our craft is a brilliant idea, but don't be limited to books for teaching. There are plenty of books exploring mathematical concepts just for the sheer fascination of it. Authors such as Alex Bellos, Matt Parker, Simon Singh and Marcus du Sautoy have multiple books well worth checking out.

- **Twitter:** Follow enough mathematics educators and eventually you will see the beautiful geometry problems from *@cshearer41* appear in your feed (or just follow her now so you don't have to wait). Memes and videos from *@howie_hua* improve any scrolling session, especially when he explains an idea like tetration (Hua, 2022), the repetition of exponentiation, and you find yourself wondering why you never even thought about it before. Jo Morgan's (*@mathsjem*) weekly *Maths Gems* blogposts frequently contain lovely tasks, puzzles and mathematical snippets you may have otherwise missed. Another good follow is *@aperiodical* for collections of mathematical news and puzzles.

- **YouTube Channels:** *Numberphile* and *3Blue1Brown* are good places to start, but Vi Hart's videos can take you from doodling a line of an infinite number of elephants across the width of a page to learning about Mersenne Primes within mere minutes.

- **Podcasts:** Andrew Jeffrey and Rob Eastaway set puzzles and explore ways mathematics crops up in everyday life in *Puzzling Mathematics*. Stand up mathematician Matt Parker and comedian Bec Hill consider a whole host of problems, like whether the famous Ferrero Rocher advert is mathematically possible, or what the optimum burger size is for your mouth in *A Problem Squared*. In *Mathematical Objects* Katie Steckles and Peter Rowlett have conversations about maths, using a wide range of objects for inspiration.

- **MathsJam:** On the second-to-last Tuesday of every month, mathematics enthusiasts meet up in various pubs across the country for MathsJam where they can share puzzles, games, problems, or just anything they think is cool or interesting. You can find details of your nearest event at https://mathsjam.com/ as well as details of the annual UK gathering, which usually takes place in November.

Enrichment

Anything we label as 'Enrichment' should be complementary to the norm, yet different from it. An after-school revision session for Year 11, for instance, is not enrichment. We really need to consider how to bring mathematics to life in the classroom and beyond, to avoid pupils viewing our lessons, and mathematics as a whole, as bland and formulaic. There is a whole host of ways in which we can spark pupils' interest and show them the wonder of mathematics, as well as illustrating links between different topics within our subject and across curriculum areas. The ideas below are grouped into categories, but in many cases they could be used for a variety of purposes.

Sources of interesting questions and tasks

- Don Steward created and shared an enormous bank of lovely mathematical questions and tasks for pretty much every topic: https://donsteward.blogspot.com/.

- Open Middle is a collection of problems which have many routes to reach the answer. By their open nature, they allow for exploration, and clever questioning can make the task more or less challenging for different pupils: https://www.openmiddle.com/.

- NRICH is the result of a collaboration between the Faculties of Mathematics and Education at the University of Cambridge. Their website is a repository of puzzles and problem-solving tasks for all stages of mathematics: https://nrich.mathematics.org/.

- Bowland Mathematics has imaginative, longer-term projects providing opportunities for rich problem-solving: https://www.bowlandmathematics.org.uk/.

Mathematics clubs

If you want to run an extracurricular mathematics club, you can find resources in the following places:

- The AMSP has a collection of activities that could be used in mathematics clubs: https://amsp.org.uk/resource/mathematics-club-activities.

- NRICH has STEM club resources: https://nrich.mathematics.org/8975.

- Think Mathematics have some lovely geometry hands-on resources, including folding hexaflexagons, building fractals, and investigating shapes of constant width: https://www.think-mathematics.co.uk/downloads.

- Pringles are a good source of mathematics! The tubes can be turned into Enigma machines (instructions can be found here: http://wiki.franklinheath.co.uk/index.php/Enigma/Paper_Enigma) and the shape of the Pringles themselves (a hyperbolic paraboloid) enables them to build a three-dimensional ring (instructions here: https://carlyandadam.com/thecarlyandadam/pringles-ring-stem-challenge)

Mathematical art

- Clarissa Grandi shares ideas to combine mathematics and art through origami, curves of pursuit, impossible shapes and more on: https://www.artfulmathematics.com.

- Islamic art provides a brilliant opportunity to explore geometry, particularly tesselations. More from the ATM here: https://www.atm.org.uk/write/MediaUploads/Conference/2019%20Conference/Speakers/Art_in_the_Mathematics_classroom.pdf.

- Pupils could be set the challenge of using Desmos online graphing software to create artwork from mathematical functions. Show them the winners of previous Desmos art contests for inspiration on: https://www.desmos.com/art.

Puzzles and games

Many puzzles and games require logical thinking. You may want to signpost these for pupils to have a go at in their spare time or explore in an after-school mathematics club, or you might just want to give them a go yourself for fun. For example, playing fractal noughts and crosses with a colleague at break time is highly recommended. In addition to tying your brains up in knots trying to outwit each other with strategy, if you happen to play it somewhere visible to the pupils (who will naturally be intrigued about what you are doing), it can open up some lovely discussions about what a fractal is.

- SET – a card game where you create sets of 3 cards where properties are either the same on all 3 cards, or different on all 3 cards. Surprisingly addictive. A free online daily puzzle can be found here to help you understand what is going on: http://www.setgame.com/set/puzzle

- Ben Orlin's book *Math Games With Bad Drawings* is a treasure trove of mathematical games to play, often requiring no more than a pen and paper.

- Simon Singh's *Parallel Project* could frankly have a section all of it its own in this chapter. His free weekly mathematics challenges (or *Parallelograms*) can be set for a whole class to attempt, or can be shared with individual pupils or parents: https://parallel.org.uk/parallelograms. Why not also investigate the *Parallel Circles* (online mathematics workshops) while you are there?

- *Sudoku*, *kakuro* and *yohaku* are different types of number puzzles where numbers have to be inserted into the correct places in a grid to meet particular rules.

Of the three, sudoku is by far the best known, although yohaku puzzles are far more interesting as they can involve a wider range of mathematical rules, such as factors, products and negative values.

- Alex Bellos writes a fortnightly puzzle column for the *Guardian*. He also invites suggestions, via email, for puzzles that he can use, so why not suggest one?

- Share a mathematics problem of the week displayed in the department, or in a weekly newsletter or on the school website. There can be prizes attached for good submissions and you can even open it up for parents to get involved as well.

Mathematics careers resources

Linking curriculum learning to careers is included in the Gatsby benchmarks for good career guidance (2014). Sometimes the links between mathematics and careers are relatively obvious, however, the simple truth is that many mathematics teachers go straight into teaching after studying for their degree, so understandably may be unaware of where and how mathematics links to various careers. Thus it is helpful to look to outside organisations for resources and experiences that can inspire and motivate pupils, raising their aspirations and awareness of potential future careers. The following resources may be helpful in supporting these goals:

- The Institute of Mathematics and its Applications has a website dedicated to sharing information and case studies about mathematics careers, and making real-world links to mathematics: https://www.mathematics careers.org.uk/.

- The AMSP has classroom resources linking mathematics to the world of work, as well as videos showcasing mathematics in different careers: https://amsp.org.uk/amsp/linking-curriculum-learning-to-careers.

- Rather than receiving second-hand information about STEM careers from their teachers, pupils could hear from STEM ambassadors instead: https://www.stem.org.uk/stem-ambassadors.

- Neon has resources to promote engineering careers: https://neonfutures.org.uk/resource/.

Trips

In addition to the suggestions below, large businesses in the local area may offer mathematical days through an educational outreach team. For example, in the North-West, Jaguar Land Rover run an education programme called *Inspiring Tomorrow's Engineers*: https://www.jaguarlandrovercareers.com/content/Education-Pathways/.

- Maths City in Leeds is a museum with interactive exhibits for pupils to explore the wonder of mathematics: https://mathematicscity.co.uk/.

- Bletchley Park in Milton Keynes is famous as the home of code-breaking during the Second World War and is fascinating to visit, as well as having beautiful grounds. You can find out more about the learning sessions they offer for different year groups here: https://bletchleypark.org.uk/event_type/learning-session/. The National Museum of Computing is also at Bletchley Park; perhaps you could organise a joint mathematics, history and computer science trip: https://www.tnmoc.org/?

Alternatively, if Bletchley Park is too far away to be feasible, you can enquire about their outreach or virtual learning sessions.

- Many theme parks and zoos now offer educational experiences, for example, Alton Towers have a STEM Learning Hub, Legoland have Education Workshops and many zoos have mathematics trails. In some cases, teachers organising a trip can visit for free beforehand to assist with their planning of the day.

- The Museum of Science and Industry in Manchester has a school's programme offering sessions for pupils from Early Years up to Key Stage 4, as well as resources for use in the classroom: https://www.scienceandindustrymuseum.org.uk/.

- Nearby, Jodrell Bank Observatory, owned and managed by the University of Manchester, is a world-leading science research institute, with scientists working at the cutting edge of modern astrophysics: https://www.jodrellbank.net/.

- The Bank of England offers tours and talks for pupils. You can also book a virtual speaker if London is too far to travel: https://www.bankofengland.co.uk/education.

Events

- The Advanced Mathematics Support Programme (AMSP) runs both online and face-to-face events including sessions about mathematics careers, as well as the excellent *Maths Inspiration* shows, which feature a variety of highly-engaging mathematical speakers, such as Hannah Fry and Matt Parker. To see what is on in your local area visit https://amsp.org.uk/events and https://mathematicsinspiration.com/home.

- Many universities have Mathematics Outreach Teams who put on events, including quizzes and 'introduction to mathematics past' school days to increase the number of pupils looking to study mathematics in the future. This is especially the case in priority areas where take-up of A Level mathematics has generally been comparatively low. Some sessions may prioritise particular groups such as girls or those in receipt of pupil premium. Contact your local universities to find what they have on offer. Some universities also run Royal Institution mathematics masterclasses, often on Saturday mornings, for high achieving 13–14 year-olds. You can find out more here: https://www.rigb.org/learning/ri-masterclasses.

In-house events

Of course, it is not always possible to organise trips out, but there are lots of ways to create a buzz around mathematics with in-house events.

- Held in November, Mathematics Week England aims to change pupils' perception of mathematics. The organisation distributes puzzles and mathematical activities for use during the week: https://mathematicsweekengland.co.uk/.

- Every February, schools across the country participate in NSPCC Number Day, with pupils sponsored for number-based activities: https://www.nspcc.org.uk/support-us/charity-fundraising/schools-fundraising-ideas/number-day/.

- Pi day is celebrated by many on 14 March with π-related activities, quizzes, digit-reciting contests and mathematical baking. Some would argue that celebrating Pi Approximation Day on 22 July would be more satisfying, but since that often falls in the summer holidays, perhaps 14 March will have to do. Mathematics teacher Chris Smith (*@aap03102*) is truly inspirational in finding increasingly elaborate ways to celebrate his love of pi with his pupils (as featured in Southall, 2022).

- Escape rooms offer lots of opportunity for problem-solving, code-cracking and logic puzzles. There are many mathematics escape room resources available online. Alternatively, School Escape Rooms can set up a mathematics-focused escape room in a classroom or in their mobile escape room van: https://www.schoolescaperooms.co.uk/.

- NRICH has sets of hands-on Mathematics Roadshow resources available for pupils of all age: https://nrich.mathematics.org/roadshow-resources.

Competitions

- The United Kingdom Mathematics Trust (UKMT) has annual mathematical problem-solving competitions for different age groups, from primary up to sixth form. There are follow-on rounds and even a summer school available for high-achieving pupils. Examples of question sets from previous challenges are available on their website, as well as information on how to register for the challenges: https://www.ukmt.org.uk/challenges.

- As well as running the events mentioned earlier, the AMSP also runs Mathematics Feasts, which are team challenges for Year 10 pupils. More information can be found here: https://amsp.org.uk/events/details/5205.

- The National Cipher Challenge, run by the University of Southampton Mathematics Department, takes place every autumn with weekly code-breaking challenges for pupils to complete. The website also contains resources for those who just want to practise without participating in the competition: https://www.cipherchallenge.org/.

- Somewhat more involved to run is the F1 in schools competition, where pupils design, build and race miniature compressed air-powered cars, raising sponsorship and managing budgets along the way. Incorporating multiple subject areas, this competition could be run in collaboration with other teachers to lighten the load: https://www.f1inschools.co.uk/.

Funding

Although some trips and competitions mentioned above incur some costs, many of the opportunities available are in fact free of charge to schools, as there are many initiatives to try to boost the uptake of mathematics courses at Key Stage 5 and university. In some cases, there might even be bursaries available to cover travel costs or teacher cover costs (the AMSP are particularly good at making their events accessible to schools running on tight budgets). It is also possible to apply for grants for STEM activities through the Royal Institution, especially if your school is in a disadvantaged area. Following a successful grant application, a STEM activity can be chosen from their list for the money to be spent on: https://www.rigb.org/learning/grants-schools

Mathematics enrichment across a trust

Sometimes academy trusts run centralised enrichment competitions that all their schools can participate in. One such example is Ormiston Academies Trust's MathOlympics competitions. These comprise of a series of individual or team challenges taking place throughout the year, encouraging pupils to use mathematical thinking, logical reasoning and creativity. The aim is for the challenges to be enjoyable to participate in, increasing pupils' enthusiasm for mathematics and helping them to view mathematics in a positive light.

Towards the end of each term, three seasonal challenges are set to be entered by pupils on an individual basis, although some schools print off the challenges and use them as activities in the classroom. One of the challenges is generally a logic problem with a seasonal theme, such as using a series of clues to determine how many Easter eggs different children found in various locations around a school on an Easter egg hunt. Often one of the challenges is some form of picture challenge, such as photographing examples of different polygons in the real world, or using Desmos graphing software to decorate an Easter egg. Other seasonal challenges have included finding the number of combinations of different coloured stripes on a T shirt, finding the value of different emojis in a grid (in a puzzle similar to the ones that often do the rounds on social media), or calculating ingredients for a super-sized chocolatey snack. Solutions to each challenge are submitted using an online form, making it easier to collect large numbers of responses. These are then filtered using a spreadsheet, with winning entries chosen at random from the correct responses.

Separate from the seasonal challenges are the MathOlympics Team Challenges. An initial challenge is set, for example, to design a mathematical board game with a geometry theme. Although multiple teams may take part in the challenge in each school, only one team per school can be put forward for a Regional Heat, with the winners then competing in a Grand Final comprising a practical challenge and quick-fire mathematics quiz, amongst other tasks. The competition is designed so that pupils from different contexts and age ranges can all compete on similar challenges, although Primary and Secondary schools compete separately in the Grand Finals of the Team Challenge.

Chapter Summary

The wealth of ideas included in this chapter may seem daunting, but that is not the intention. Rather the hope is that there is plenty to pique the interest of the reader, whoever they may be and in whatever context they are working. Not all readers will be interested in all the ideas mentioned, in much the same way as not all pupils will connect with every idea, but in finding different ways to share our passion for mathematics with our pupils, we hope that we might spark a little passion for the subject in them too. Part of the fun is in exploring enough to find whatever aspect it is that makes us pause and think, *'Wow! Isn't mathematics wonderful…'*

- Remember that enrichment should be part of a well-rounded curriculum, not just a bolt-on.
- All pupils deserve enriching experiences, not just the highest achieving.
- The more we extend our own knowledge and understanding of mathematics, the more likely we are to discover interesting ideas to incorporate into our teaching.

FURTHER READING

Anthony Lo Bello's *Origins of Mathematical Words* (2013). If mathematical etymology is your thing then this is an essential point of reference. Alternatively, you may find this online etymology dictionary of use: https://www.etymonline.com/.

Luetta Reimer & Wilbert Reimer, *Mathematicians Are People, Too* (1990). Stories about some great mathematicians that really bring them to life in a way which is accessible to pupils and teachers alike.

Alex Bellos, *Alex's Adventures in Numberland* (2010). An accessible book packed full of fascinating mathematical ideas and how they underpin our everyday lives.

Talithia Williams, PhD *Power in Numbers: The Rebel Women of Mathematics* (2018). If you think all mathematicians are dead white men, then you clearly haven't read *Mathematicians Are People, Too*, but if you want to well and truly dispel that myth then this book should do the trick.

For a comprehensive overview of the history of mathematics, searchable by mathematician, culture, topic and more, you cannot beat St. Andrew's University's MacTutor History of Mathematics Archive: https://mathematicshistory.st-andrews.ac.uk

Leila Schenps' *Math on Trial: How Numbers Get Used and Abused in the Courtroom* (2013) uses real cases to highlight the dangers of carelessly sprinkling mathematics over real-world problems and how we can be manipulated by statistics.

Matt Parker, *Humble Pi: A Comedy of Mathematics Errors* (2019). Exposing the mathematical mishaps and the consequences they have had on our everyday life.

Simon Singh has written many books to explore:

Fermat's Last Theorem (1997). After Pierre de Fermat scrawled in his margin *'I have a truly marvellous demonstration of this proposition which this margin is too narrow to contain'*, the mathematics community relentlessly attempted to provide the proof for his eponymous Last Theorem. In 1993, English mathematician Andrew Wiles announced that he had finally cracked it. This book tells his story and the many endeavours that came before him.

The Code Book: The Secret History of Codes and Code-breaking (1999). Reveals the incredible stories throughout time of those who have made codes and those you have broken them.

The Simpsons and their Mathematics Secrets (2013). The writers of *The Simpsons* have been sneaking mathematics into their show for decades. This book will take you through the history of some of the mathematics featured in their show.

Rob Eastaway also has a fabulous collection, including *Mathematics on the Back of an Envelope* (2019), an introduction to the invaluable art of estimation, *Why do Buses Come in Threes?* (1998, co-authored with Jeremy Wyndham) and its sequel *How long is a piece of string?* (2002), which illuminate the hidden mathematics in everyday events, ranging from the days of the week to magic tricks.

7

Applying science and research to teaching mathematics

The twentieth century saw a surge of empirical and qualitative research into teaching and learning. The learning of mathematics was studied extensively during this time and we now benefit from theory and evidence from the fields of education research and cognitive psychology, helping us to find ways to help more pupils successfully learn mathematics.

The concept of 'how to teach mathematics' is far from settled. There are debates around the philosophy of education, the purpose of teaching mathematics, and even the content that should and should not be included at school level, that probably preclude us from reaching total consensus any time soon. That said, there is still more than enough that we know about cognition in general, about the structure of mathematical knowledge, and about foundational concepts, to allow us to approach 'best bets' in teaching mathematics. In this chapter, we will take a short tour around these knowns so that you can shape your practice accordingly.

Evolutionary psychology

Social learning, where animals imitate the behaviours of those around them, is observable in many species, yet humans stand out in our capacity, through imitation and teaching, to pass on behaviours, artefacts and technologies that become more complex or effective over time. Knowledge is one such artefact. In transmitting knowledge, new generations can iterate, change, discover and create. Books and other technologies allow us to store knowledge over time. Universal free schooling allows everyone to engage in our shared knowledge and in the positive cultural consequences of greater learning. As such, it serves us well to make schooling for all as successful as possible.

David Geary, in *Educating the Evolved Mind* (2007), discusses a distinction of two types of knowledge. Biologically primary knowledge may be thought of as 'folk' knowledge that we acquire through our interactions with others and which the overwhelming majority of us acquire through simply being in society. This contrasts with biologically secondary knowledge, the knowledge that needs to be taught and which needs personal effort to be learnt. Speech is considered primary, as is walking, or a sense of humour. Reading and writing are secondary. We need secondary knowledge to function as a successful member of a highly evolved society and deliberate instruction is the only way to guarantee this knowledge is acquired by the majority of people.

Some parts of mathematical thought are biologically primary. We develop a sense of magnitude and a comprehension of small counting numbers without needing formal instruction. If we put two apples on the left and five apples on the right and ask a toddler, *'Which is more?'* they can tell you without counting. We understand that successive counting increases a quantity by one without needing a formal numerical system to help us think about this. Thus, basic numerosity can be thought of as a primary ability. In contrast, the formal base ten numerical system, the ability to describe numbers far beyond a magnitude we can naturally conceptualise, proportional reasoning, the geometry we use to describe the space of the world and the use of an algebraic symbol system to generalise what we know about numbers are all biologically secondary. They have been invented and discovered over thousands of years and must be carefully and consciously passed on to the next generation. So we see that school mathematics is a largely secondary domain of knowledge that builds upon a small but significant primary domain.

Geary uses his theory as a motivation for teaching. In his own words, '*The cognitive and motivational complexities of the processes involved in the generation of secondary knowledge and the ever-widening gap between this knowledge and folk knowledge leads me to conclude that most children will not be sufficiently motivated nor cognitively able to learn all of the secondary knowledge needed for functioning in modern societies without well organized, explicit and direct teacher instruction.*'

Extending Geary's conclusion, one of the most important things teachers can do is understand how pupils learn, and how they learn mathematics, so that we can make optimal use of the limited time they have with us, inducting them into the mathematical knowledge needed to function in society and, where possible, enabling them to contribute to its advancement.

Cognitive load theory

Cognitive psychologists study how our brains process, store, forget and remember information in an effort to understand more about learning. Since the 1950s we have known that our short-term memory, now called working memory, is very limited (Miller, 1956). To demonstrate this, take a moment to work out the answer to this calculation in your head and reflect on your method.

$$56 \times 3$$

Perhaps you used distributivity to find 50×3 and 6×3 and add them together. You have the necessary knowledge in your long-term memory to find these two products and their sum, so your working memory can use this stored information to solve the problem. Now take another moment and find the answer to this one.

$$47{,}865 \times 3$$

This time, you probably struggled, but not because the component parts are any harder. You can do $40{,}000 \times 3$ and 7000×3 and 800×3 and 60×3 and 5×3, but to hold the answer to so many constituent parts in your head while you add on more is extremely difficult. The second problem contains so many more chunks for your brain to think about in one go that you experience a high cognitive load, most likely overload, and you cannot reach the answer.

Someone who has not memorised their multiplication tables will struggle with 56×3 as they do not have the requisite knowledge in long-term memory, so exhausting their working memory with the first step of 50×3. The importance of working memory and long-term memory has been extensively studied over the last 50 or so years, and one of the most useful ideas to come forth is that of John Sweller's Cognitive Load Theory (CLT), proposed in the 1980s and 90s and much studied since (see Sweller, 1994).

CLT gives teachers a framework for instruction that aims to optimise the load placed on pupils during the learning process, therefore optimising the chances of learning happening. It is not a complete theory of instruction, nor does it address every aspect of what happens in the classroom. It is, however, essential for us to understand as it deals with one of the central principles of teaching: how we can increase the chances of pupils processing the information that is important.

There are three types of cognitive load: intrinsic, extraneous and germane. Intrinsic load refers to the inherent complexity of the material to be learned. Some mathematics is inherently more complex than others and this complexity is variable dependent on the prior knowledge of the learner. Take these two equations:

$$(A) \quad 2x + 3 = 10$$
$$(B) \quad 2x + 3 = 4x + 10$$

For someone who can solve a basic linear equation such as (A), an equation such as (B) has a degree of intrinsic load lower than for the person still struggling to solve (A). This intrinsic load is a function of element interactivity. CLT uses the term 'element' for something that needs to be learned, including facts, concepts and procedures. If you can learn an element without much need to refer to other elements (such as memorising the times tables – you can learn that $7 \times 4 = 28$ without having to think about the fact that $2 \times 6 = 12$), then the task has low element interactivity and is said to impose a small cognitive load. If you cannot learn an element without also thinking about lots of other elements (such as solving an equation when you are still getting your head around the concept of variables and inverse operations), then the task has high element interactivity and imposes a greater cognitive load. Thus, if you are confident in solving (A), then there is a small step to being able to solve (B) and the element interactivity is low. If you need to think hard about (A), then the element interactivity of (B) is increased and the intrinsic cognitive load is high.

In order to increase the chances of learning, we must reduce intrinsic load to an appropriate level. This means we must teach pupils the right mathematics at the right time. If we try to teach someone mathematics for which a lack of prior knowledge causes high intrinsic load, we are setting them up to struggle. The idea of intrinsic load compels us to learn about our pupils – what they know, what they can and cannot do – and to meet them where they are, not where we think they should be. This means giving them tasks that are just on the edge of their knowledge, something we have mentioned in various places throughout this book.

Extraneous load is load imposed external to the content to be learnt. Some of the most obvious causes of extraneous load are distractors in the environment. If people are talking around us while we are trying to concentrate, we easily lose track of what we are focusing on. Extrapolate to the classroom and we can see why a noisy environment is not conducive to concentration and, therefore, learning. Some people have argued that wall displays are an environmental factor causing extraneous cognitive load. This may or may not be the case. Displays that remain in place for a long period of time will often be tuned out by pupils and distractions caused by them are likely to be short-lived. Does the benefit of a welcoming environment outweigh the distraction it might cause? This is a question for discussion, but probably belongs more in the realm of teacher workload: excessive time should not be spent on creating displays that will be mainly ignored.

The more important facet of extraneous load for a teacher to consider is instruction itself. The way we teach can induce cognitive load or can reduce it, so it is paramount that we pay careful attention to how we teach, what we say, how we move (wandering around the classroom while talking the pupils through a process means they have to focus on both what you are saying and where you are, whereas standing still in one place removes one of the factors competing for their attention) and how we expect pupils to participate in the instruction. This is where CLT has birthed a number of well-evidenced effects to help us understand effective instruction, which we will discuss later.

The third type of cognitive load, termed germane load, is the one of the three that should be increased, not decreased. This is the good type of load, that means pupils are thinking hard about the right kinds of things, putting effort into building a strong schema, or mental network of knowledge. There is no easy way to tell what constitutes germane load, but we can tell that once work becomes too easy, or too automatic, it is unlikely that a pupil is experiencing germane load. This brings us back to the idea of the right tasks at the right time. Tasks that help pupils to automate procedures are good in initial learning, but we must ensure that we are always pushing our pupils to learn more about the topic at hand, linking it to previously learnt concepts and increasing their depth of understanding, rather than simply giving them more of the same. We discussed the idea of using different types of tasks and thinking at different stages of learning in Chapter 5 when we looked at problem solving and reasoning, and now we have further evidence for those ideas from the realm of cognitive load theory.

In the next few sections, we will look in a little more depth at how we can reduce extraneous load and increase germane load.

The worked example effect

Studying worked examples has been shown to have a positive effect on pupils' initial learning when compared to giving pupils problems to solve (Cooper and Sweller, 1987). The use of worked examples allows pupils to focus on the individual components of new learning, reducing element interactivity and therefore cognitive load. In comparison, giving pupils problems to solve can split their attention across multiple possible alternatives and can reduce their chance of successfully getting to grips with new content. This is not to say that problems are not important, but that we should use them with careful consideration (see Chapter 5).

Using worked examples is commonplace in mathematics classrooms, but not all worked examples are created equal. When choosing examples, ask yourself these questions:

- What do I want pupils to see from this example?
- Which numbers will illustrate this best (and which might obscure it, see Chapter 2)?
- What will I say?
- What will I write?
- What will I ask pupils to do?
- What do I want pupils to think about? (This is, arguably, the most important question.)

Take this example, intended to explain what it means to square a number:

$$2^2 = 4$$

A pupil could infer from this example that squaring means multiplying by two and then give the answer to 3^2 as 6. Using a different base and a few more examples, before looking at 2^2 as an interesting case, highlighting the possible misconception that could arise from it, would be much more beneficial.

Imagine you are teaching your pupils about the circle theorem that states, *'the angle at the centre is double the angle at the circumference subtended by the same arc'*. You use this as your example.

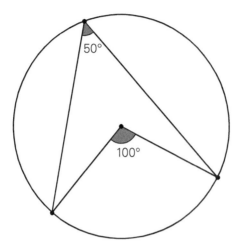

You then ask pupils to copy out the example into their book and try a similar one, like this:

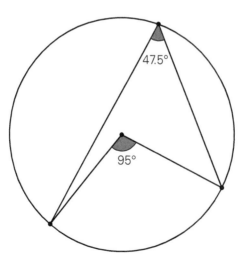

They then complete a set of questions of similar presentation, until they get stuck with this:

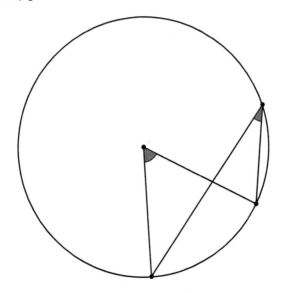

There are a number of points in this teaching episode where thinking about CLT can help us to improve pupils' learning. It is important that pupils try some similar questions and you have the chance to check their understanding (see Chapter 3), but including a more complex example early on, like the question immediately above, will more likely make pupils think about the geometric structure of the theorem, rather than focus on recognising the most basic presentation of it. Introducing this difficulty from the start is an example of the variability effect (Paas and van Merriënboer, 1994), which induces germane load. The variability effect tells us that exposure to a greater range of examples, where we can compare and contrast features of a concept or procedure, yields an increase in performance. Drawing attention to different presentations of the same theorem from the start, accompanied with questions such as, *'What is the same? What is different?'* encourages pupils to concentrate on the deep, or underlying, structure of the theorem rather than imitating one limited example. Dynamic geometry software such as Geogebra is powerful here, as it allows you to demonstrate boundary examples with ease.

Once the example has been demonstrated, it can be useful to ask pupils to explain each step to themselves – what happened here? Why did we do that? The self-explanation effect has been shown to help pupils to make sense of what they have just seen and is much more effective than simply asking them to copy the example into their book. In fact, there is little benefit to copying examples into books at all, especially if doing so takes a long time (as it would if they had to sketch circles!). Given the ubiquity of free, explanatory videos on the internet for every topic in school mathematics, we suggest that the time taken up in classrooms throughout the country on copying worked examples would be better spent in self-explanation, a period of teacher-led formative assessment to check for understanding, or simply practising more questions. (The often-used argument that an exercise book should become a revision guide is not convincing in mathematics, where the best revision is more practice, all of which is available in workbooks or online.)

When using worked examples, a teacher's choice of words and actions is very important. Taking our circle theorem example, we should identify why the angles are subtended by the same arc, perhaps by highlighting the line segments that form the angles, showing how they originate at the same points on the circumference, so that our pupils understand what makes this theorem as it is, rather than looking for a familiar arrowhead shape. The questions pupils complete should include various presentations of the theorem so that pupils get used to its structure from the beginning. It is also a good idea to gradually interleave questions involving other circle theorems already learnt so that pupils start to differentiate between them, comparing and contrasting their features. The psychologists Elizabeth and Robert Björk (2011) call interleaving a *'desirable difficulty'* – something which increases the germane load of a task and makes for stronger long-term learning.

In the brilliant book, *Teaching Math with Examples* (2021), Michael Pershan sets out the case for quality worked examples and how to use them effectively in the classroom. One of Pershan's main messages is that pupils need to be thinking *actively* and *deeply* about the mathematics we want them to learn, and that good use of worked examples can help them to do this by focusing them on what is important. He advocates printing out worked examples and asking pupils to complete self-explanation prompts before posing related problems for pupils to work on to check their understanding.

The split-attention effect and dual coding

Standard exam questions on geometry tend to present an image with text underneath explaining the relevant mathematical details.

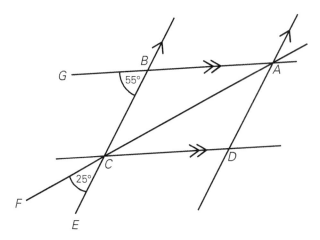

ABCD is a parallelogram.
ABG, BCE and ACF are straight lines.
Angle GBC = 55°
Angle FCE = 25°

Find the size of angle CAD.
Give a reason for each stage of your working.

Presenting questions like this during *initial* learning can lead to cognitive load caused by the split-attention effect. Pupils have to look at the text and the diagram separately in order to fully process the question and this makes it harder for them to make sense of the scenario. If we want our pupils to learn to relate the words accurately to the diagram, we should present the words step-by-step, adjacent to the relevant part of the diagram and use highlighting to link the text to the image.

ABCD is a parallelogram.

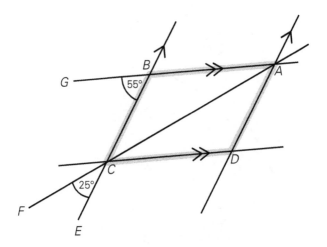

ABCD is a parallelogram.
ABG, *BCE* and *ACF* are straight lines.

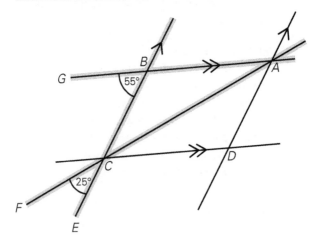

ABCD is a parallelogram.
ABG, *BCE* and *ACF* are straight lines.

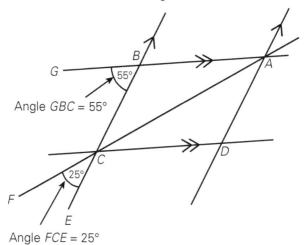

Angle *GBC* = 55°

Angle *FCE* = 25°

ABCD is a parallelogram.
ABG, *BCE* and *ACF* are straight lines.

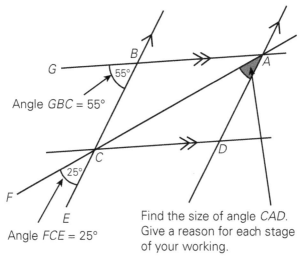

Angle *GBC* = 55°

Angle *FCE* = 25°

Find the size of angle *CAD*.
Give a reason for each stage
of your working.

This also applies to working out solutions in the early stages of learning. It is better for pupils to annotate the diagram with angles they find until they reach an answer and, once they have got to grips with the angle facts they need to use, only then work on how to set out a solution in a clear, written way. Treating 'applying the mathematics to find the answer' and 'communicating the solution clearly' as two different, yet related pursuits can help us to reduce cognitive load on pupils.

In a similar vein, dual coding tells us that visuals and words together can be more powerful than one or the other, so telling pupils to annotate diagrams with important mathematical information, rather than write the information out separately, can help them to learn more easily. This aspect of dual coding applies to the idea of concrete and pictorial representations.

Concrete and pictorial representations

Humans remember concrete information better than abstract information (Paivio et al., 1994). Mathematics is highly abstract, so we have developed ways of making the abstract more concrete in order to make it more accessible to more pupils. Chapter 4 goes into these concrete representations in a lot of detail, but here it is worth pointing out that concrete representations, such as algebra tiles or Dienes blocks, are more than just a tool to help those who struggle. They tap into the fact that every single one of us learns better when we can make the abstract tangible and easier to imagine. Representations can be seen as a form of dual coding if used alongside formal, written mathematics. For example, the idea of completing the square is more accessible and, arguably, memorable, if learnt like this:

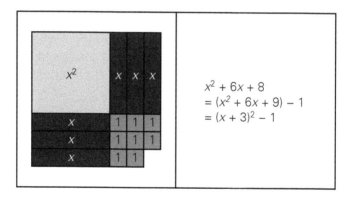

By writing the symbolic algebra alongside a visual representation, we can help pupils to make sense of the concept more readily as they process it in two complementary ways together.

Expertise reversal and guidance fading

When pupils first learn an idea, we call them novice. Over time and with practice, which increases fluency and builds connections – in other words, practice that builds their mathematical schema – pupils become more expert. The expertise reversal effect tells us that novices learn best from clear instruction which includes worked examples. As expertise grows, however, worked examples can cause a cognitive load that actually hinders learning, as they draw attention to redundant information that is hard to ignore (Sweller et al., 2003). It is at this point that pupils benefit from less structure in tasks and are better placed for solving problems (there is a fuller discussion of this in Chapter 5).

The guidance fading effect is a direct consequence of expertise reversal. It tells us that as expertise grows, pupils should be moved from worked examples, to scaffolded questions, to full (unscaffolded) questions (Renkl and Atkinson, 2003). The guidance fading effect can also be used to help pupils access worked examples and multi-step procedures using something called backwards fading, which we talked about in Chapter 3 in the context of adapting teaching to help all pupils to achieve.

The table below sets out a series of questions for a pupil that are backwards faded, scaffolding the process to make it more easily accessible.

Long-term memory

At the start of the chapter, we looked at the usefulness of having multiplication facts stored in long-term memory. If you know the multiplication tables, then working with any other area of mathematics that requires them becomes much easier – you can simplify fractions, factorise a quadratic or calculate scaled

Question 1	Question 2	Question 3	Question 4
Solve the equation $x^2 + 5x + 6 = 0$	Solve the equation $x^2 + 7x + 12 = 0$	Solve the equation $x^2 + 6x + 5 = 0$	Solve the equation $x^2 + 3x + 2 = 0$
$x^2 + 5x + 6 = 0$	$x^2 + 7x + 12 = 0$		
$(x + 3)(x + 2) = 0$	$(x + 3)(x + 4) = 0$	$x^2 + 6x + 5 = 0$	
$x = -3$ or $x = \underline{\quad}$	$x = \underline{\quad}$ or $x = \underline{\quad}$	$(x + \underline{\quad})(x + \underline{\quad}) = 0$	

quantities in a recipe quicker than you could without these facts. Having knowledge in our long-term memory frees up working memory to concentrate on the new learning at hand.

From Piaget in 1952, psychologists have used the term 'schema' to refer to the way we organise knowledge. Our schema of mathematics consists of the facts and procedures that we learn, but also the concepts that underpin them and the connections between those concepts. This combination of procedural and conceptual knowledge is the web of mathematics stored in our long-term memory. When we first learn, our knowledge is surface-level, or inflexible. Over time and with quality practice, it becomes deeper and more connected to other knowledge, or flexible (see Chapter 5 for more discussion on this).

The problem with our long-term memories is that they do not last forever. We all forget things over time. Herman Ebbinghaus (1885) was the first to publish ideas around forgetting, producing the eponymous 'forgetting curve', which suggests that we forget information quickly but less so the more we revisit it. Although nothing close to a rigorous study by modern standards, the idea of Ebbinghaus's 'forgetting curve' helps us to think about how to structure periods of teaching. It is tempting to think that forgetting is a bad thing, but this is not necessarily the right conclusion to make. Perhaps we never really forget things. Or perhaps forgetting is not the same as losing knowledge, but rather losing immediate access to it.

Elizabeth and Robert Björk's New Theory of Disuse (1992) builds on this idea, defining two measures of memory strength: storage strength and retrieval strength. If you have learned something well, it has a high storage strength. If you can bring it to mind quickly and easily, it has a high retrieval strength. If your pupils have just learnt how to find the mean of a set of numbers, it will have a low storage strength but a high retrieval strength. A couple of days later, both the storage and retrieval strengths will be low. If they then spend some more lessons practising finding the mean, applying it to different scenarios, interpreting it and solving problems with it, then their storage strength will be greatly increased. After a term, you might ask them a question using the mean and your pupils cannot remember what to do but, after a quick reminder, can access tasks with as much success as they could originally. This tells you their storage strength was still high, but their retrieval strength low.

Classroom tasks that are varied, that take pupils to depth of understanding, that show them where a procedure is and is not applicable, all contribute to storage strength. Learning something in depth is a very good thing. Over time, tasks that remind pupils of what they have learnt, so that they practise retrieving it from memory, will improve their retrieval strength, keeping it 'at the front of their minds'. They will then be more likely to be able to use this learning in novel contexts, or in other areas of mathematics that require it.

Spacing

One such type of 'retrieval practice' is spacing, where we come back to practise what we have learnt at spaced intervals. In the classroom, this might mean that we learn about mean, mode and median in our 'averages' unit and then we use small parts of subsequent lessons over the coming weeks and months to practise finding these averages. We might also set periodic homework tasks on the topic. The important thing is that we can gradually reduce the frequency of these retrieval episodes as our pupils' retrieval strength increases.

It is important to note here that, due to its hierarchical nature, much of the mathematics we teach is naturally and automatically spaced. As we noted earlier, once pupils have learnt to multiply, their knowledge is applied repeatedly and over intervals in the context of new learning: fractions, expressions, proportional reasoning and more.

There are things we can do to increase the effect of this type of natural spacing. For instance, if we have taught pupils to calculate with decimals and fractions, we can deliberately include decimal and fraction calculations in future units, say, on finding area and perimeter, or calculating averages. Be mindful of this opportunity: by exploiting it wherever possible we can save other episodes of retrieval practice (like our starter activities or low-stakes quizzes) for those topics that do not lend themselves so naturally to this kind of assimilation.

The testing effect

Repeated studies have shown that learning is increased by testing rather than merely studying material (for example, Karpicke and Roediger III, 2008). We are not talking about sitting assessments or exams here, rather giving pupils opportunities to try and recall things by 'quizzing' themselves or being quizzed.

This has implications for classroom practice and, in particular, what we might put under the banner of retrieval practice. In the context of improving long-term memory, making pupils think hard to pull things from memory is superior to activities where they can rely on their book, or their peers. If you are giving pupils a quiz on topics they have been studying, it is better in most cases that they work independently and with a closed book. If retrieval strength is so low that they cannot access the questions at all, then they will need prompts, or a quick demonstration, but they should then be given opportunity to test themselves in subsequent retrieval practice sessions until they can recall and apply their knowledge reliably. Remember: the goal of retrieval practice is to improve pupils' long-term memory and, in particular, their retrieval strength. If what you are doing in the classroom is not achieving this, rethink how you do it.

Mathematical cognition

Mathematical cognition is a relatively new research field, emerging in the twenty-first century and combining the disciplines of experimental psychology, education and neuroscience to try and understand the cognitive processes behind acquisition of mathematical knowledge so that we can better explain individual differences in performance and structure instruction to help pupils to be more successful.

Mathematical cognition research tells us, for instance, that children's conceptions of the equals sign can impact their later success with equations and equivalence (see, for example, McNeil and Alibali, 2005). Those who have an 'operational' conception, where they see = as meaning something like 'do the operation and put the answer here,' are less likely to be successful in solving equations than those with a 'relational' conception, where they see = as meaning something like 'the expressions on either side are equivalent and whatever I do to one side I must do to the other'. Insights like this can help us to concentrate on using class time to develop conceptions that lead to future success.

The field of mathematical cognition is broad. For instance, we know from it that conceptual and procedural knowledge develop in tandem and complement each other (see, for example, Rittle-Johnson and Schneider, 2015), bringing implications for classroom instruction and curriculum design (see Chapter 9). We also know that mathematics anxiety reduces working memory capacity, thus slowing down learning further, prompting us to employ practices that reduce anxiety in the classroom (and to challenge anyone in an influential position who makes light of being 'no good at' mathematics).

Another interesting finding is the idea of the natural number bias: where people are so used to working with the natural numbers that they apply the 'rules' of natural numbers to places where they are not valid (see, for example, Obersteiner et al., 2013). We see this when pupils struggle to solve an equation which has a negative or fractional answer, thinking that it 'doesn't work', or when they think that multiplication always makes a number larger, because that is what they see with the natural numbers. One way to reduce the natural number bias is to normalise working with decimals, fractions and irrational numbers, using them throughout topics so that they are not seen as separate or different.

Chapter Summary

Throughout this chapter we have considered how academic research in cognitive science can be applied to teaching and learning mathematics. Our discussion is nowhere near exhaustive, and teaching is a craft that can only be improved through experience. What we have, however, is a broad set of principles from which to start.

- Always teach pupils on the edge of their current understanding. Use tasks and activities that increase their knowledge and make links between things they have learnt before.
- Teach with attention to cognitive load. Reduce intrinsic load by teaching pupils things when they are ready to process them well. Reduce extraneous load by reducing distractors in the environment and in tasks themselves. Increase germane load by using the right kinds of tasks at the right time – less directed as pupils become more expert.
- Take time for pupils to get to grips with concepts and procedures, and teach for depth of understanding at first, giving strong storage strength. After this, use tasks that allow pupils to revisit their learning periodically, increasing retrieval strength.
- Use worked examples in ways that optimise their utility, thinking carefully about your numbers, your explanations and the activity you want pupils to be engaged in.
- Look into findings from mathematical cognition that focus specifically on how people learn mathematics. Use these to guide your instruction.

FURTHER READING

Craig Barton's *How I Wish I'd Taught Maths* (2018) delves into aspects of cognitive science and how they specifically apply in our subject.

In *What Every Teacher Needs To Know About Psychology* (2016), David Didau and Nick Rose give a general overview of cognitive load theory and the cognitive effects that come from it.

For a good insight into the current major findings in the field of mathematical cognition, take a look at *An Introduction to Mathematical Cognition* (2018) by Camilla Gilmore, Silke M Göbel and Matthew Inglis.

To explore how worked examples can be used to greatest effect, have a read of the short but powerful *Teaching Math With Examples* (2021) from Michael Pershan.

8

Personal professional development

As educators, we are in the business of learning. It is our job to understand how children learn and apply our understanding to teaching them well. As we hope you will have seen through this book so far, understanding is not a 'yes/no' dichotomy – it does not make sense to say someone does or does not understand something. Instead, understanding is something that gains depth over time, through learning. This applies to us as teachers as well as to our pupils as learners. Our quality and success as teachers is directly related to our knowledge of teaching, and teacher quality matters. In fact, it is the most important predictor of pupil attainment (Rice, 2003). No teacher can ever be the finished product, as there is no such thing as a finished product, and it is important that we continue to learn, so that we can be the best version of ourselves for the pupils we teach. Great professional development will improve us as teachers and, as a consequence, will improve our pupils' learning.

Defining what 'effective teacher quality' looks like can be complex (and sometimes controversial). It is difficult to measure purely on pupil outcomes, as results are often the product of five or more different teachers over the course of a pupil's years of secondary schooling, and not just down to the teacher during the exam year. There are a range of factors that contribute to overall effective teacher quality.

It is essential to have strong subject knowledge for the key stage you are teaching, with a deep pedagogical understanding of the content. These two things are different and should not be treated synonymously; as we saw in Chapters 1 and 4, *teaching* mathematics is different from *doing* mathematics. Mathematics-specific pedagogical knowledge can include having a range of different ways to communicate a concept or idea, knowing the prerequisite knowledge of the lesson's content, being able to pre-empt where pupils will get stuck, being fluent in a range of different methods for a procedure, and understanding why and how they work, and knowing how to represent the abstract in an accessible way. On top of this, general pedagogical skills such as behaviour management and creating a positive learning environment are essential. Striving for the intersection of all three is key. In this chapter, we will explore ways you can develop each of these factors of quality teaching through professional development.

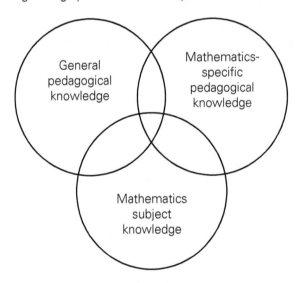

Deepening your mathematics subject knowledge

In the 2014 Sutton Trust report *What makes great teaching?*, authors conclude that *'the most effective teachers have deep knowledge of the subjects they teach, and when teachers' knowledge falls below a certain level it is a significant impediment to pupils' learning'* (Coe et al., 2014, p. 2). Cast your mind back to how you were taught to divide fractions at school. When you started training to teach, had you ever thought about *why* the process you were taught works or what the underlying structure of it was? If you answered yes, you are probably in the minority. Even the most knowledgeable mathematics graduate will have limited depth of knowledge of school mathematics – they learn it as a pupil and move onto other things, never needing to think about the basics in depth again. It is precisely this depth of knowledge, however, that helps us to know *how* to teach something well – how to build connections and explain things in ways that are accessible to hundreds of different pupils. Once we start teaching, we must accept our responsibility to keep learning about our subject. Fortunately, there are many ways to do this.

- Read some books on subject knowledge, ideally those aimed at teachers rather than just textbooks. Ed Southall's *Yes, But Why? Teaching for understanding in mathematics* (2017) and Jemma Sherwood's *How To Enhance Your Mathematics Subject Knowledge: Number and algebra for secondary teachers* (2018) are both a good place to begin working on your depth of subject knowledge for school-level mathematics. If you want to explore different methods, their similarities and differences, then Jo Morgan's *A Compendium Of Mathematical Methods* (2019) is the place to start.

- Complete a subject knowledge audit – start a list, with any topics you are unsure of and wouldn't feel comfortable teaching. Working through past exam papers or a textbook can help you to identify these topics.

- Seek support – ask to observe other teachers when they are teaching those topics, or for them to explain the part(s) you are unsure of. Practise the mathematics the same way you would encourage your pupils to practise.

- Attend the courses and conferences signposted later in this chapter.

- Scrutinise mark schemes to learn how marks are awarded to working out in exams. Check the alternative methods in the mark schemes – there might be some that you are not aware of.

- Read the DfE's mathematics programmes of study and the exam boards' specifications to have a full understanding of the statutory requirements and how they will be assessed. It is crucial that we also dedicate time to best understand where the mathematics we teach is going and how it has built on what came before, so do this for the key stages that follow and precede the ones you teach.

- Invest in your own mathematical enrichment – visit Bletchley Park if you've never had the chance or start a departmental book club featuring the books we recommend later in the chapter.

Increasing your mathematics-specific pedagogical knowledge

As we have discussed throughout this book, subject knowledge alone is not enough to teach mathematics well. We need to develop a robust knowledge of strong ways to communicate mathematics to our pupils and strong ways for them to make meaning of what we teach. The 'What makes great teaching?' report tells us that, *As well as a strong understanding of the material being taught, teachers must also understand the ways pupils think about the content, be able to evaluate the thinking behind pupils' own methods and identify pupils' common misconceptions.*' (Coe et al., 2014, p. 2) The knowledge of how to teach mathematics in the wider (national and international) mathematics community is always growing. Cognitive psychologists are working to discover the mental mechanisms that underpin mathematical thinking, researchers in instructional design are iterating curricula to improve them all the time, and teachers get together in work groups and communities – in-person and online – to share knowledge. Since the body of knowledge around mathematical cognition and teaching and learning mathematics is ever-growing, so will our own knowledge and practice grow if we devote time to learning and trying things in the classroom. Here are some of the ways we can improve our mathematics-specific pedagogy.

- Professional reflection is the first thing we must take time to do. Analyse your lessons, interrogating your own actions by asking yourself what the pupils understood and what they struggled with. Dedicate time to understand your curriculum, so that you are happy to articulate why the content is sequenced in this order, how is it connected, what consistency the department might have in methods or representations, and why they have been chosen. Discussions with your department or your wider network can help to align or challenge your thinking.

- Read lots of books. Emma McCrea's *Making Every Maths Lesson Count* (2019) contains 52 evidence- and experience-informed strategies for, well, making every maths lesson count, while Tony Gardiner's *Teaching Mathematics at Secondary Level* (2016) analyses the National Curriculum in terms of how pupils learn the content.

- Listen to podcasts. Craig Barton's is a great place to start, with a huge back catalogue of interviews with maths teachers and others involved in education.

- Sign up to be become an examiner. You will receive training from the exam board on how to mark each question, developing your knowledge of mark schemes and methods. You will also see, first hand, the different approaches pupils use and the misconceptions and mistakes that prevent them from being successful. Share what you learn with your colleagues so that it informs more than your own teaching.

- Read examiner reports, freely available on every exam board's website. They highlight the common errors and misconceptions pupils have made on a wider sample.

Increasing your general pedagogical knowledge

The full benefit of our subject and pedagogical knowledge can only be felt in a classroom with a positive culture, where pupils are enabled to learn free from distraction and negative influences.

General pedagogical knowledge allows us to create such a classroom, and every single teacher is capable of becoming more skilled in designing and maintaining a classroom that is conducive to learning if they dedicate attention to improving these skills. To know more about how to create a classroom that promotes learning and that helps all children to make good progress, you would do well to start with some of these resources.

- Read Doug Lemov's *Teach Like a Champion* (TLAC). This book offers specific, clearly explained techniques for any teacher to implement in their classroom immediately. The techniques offer a shared vocabulary that you can use across your department or school. There are accompanying videos of teachers demonstrating the techniques in their classroom and you can freely access the author's field notes on his fantastic blog at https://teachlikeachampion.org/blog/.

- For sound behaviour management advice, read Tom Bennett's *Running the Room*.

Barriers to overcome

Personal development is not without barriers or difficulties. Here are some that you may encounter and some advice to overcome them.

- **Time:** Time is a precious and inelastic resource. It can be tempting to focus on tasks that seem more immediate – administrative tasks, marking and the like – but these can hog all our time. Deliberately schedule time into your week to focus on your own knowledge development. Protect the time and don't let something else take it. The quality of your instruction will improve if you do.

- **Cost:** Not all the professional development recommended above is free. Don't be afraid to ask schools to fund your professional development, particularly if it links to your targets; many schools are more than willing to supplement the price of professional development to improve teacher quality. You could suggest to your head of department or SLT that some money be used for a departmental library, then share the books between the team. You could even have a 'book club' where you use some meeting time to discuss an extract you have all read in advance.

- **Change:** Things change over time as new evidence is brought to attention. Always be prepared to iterate your existing mental models of teaching and learning. If you only do what you have always done, you risk missing out on becoming a better practitioner. Learning more about teaching and increasing our own knowledge base makes the job fascinating and rewarding.

- **Fear of failure:** Making mistakes is okay; just learn from them. A reflective practitioner understands that nothing will ever be perfect. Once you accept this and determine to learn from what happens in your classroom, you start to lose the fear of failure. Researcher and educator Dylan Wiliam (2019) says, *'We all fail as teachers because we have such high hopes for our pupils. But the teacher who does not think she or he can get better blames this failure on the pupils. "What can you expect from pupils from* *that part of town?," "From that estate?," "With those kinds of parents?" They fail because all teachers fail, but teachers with a fixed mindset blame this failure on the pupils: "I taught it, they just didn't learn it." '* Understanding that we have a huge amount of control over what happens in our classrooms empowers us to make things better for all and stops us putting blame onto others or things outside our control.

- **Cynicism:** When you have been teaching a long time, you see ideas come and go. Instead of throwing out every new suggestion that comes your way, thinking it'll pass quick enough, critically evaluate them in the light of your existing knowledge. If an idea can be assimilated into what you know is successful, give it a try. If it challenges your existing conceptions, analyse it – be prepared that your existing conceptions might not be as good as the new idea, just as the new idea might not be as good as your existing conceptions.

- **Lack of coherence:** The longer we teach, the more connected our schema of teaching and learning becomes. If we take other people's isolated tips and 'tricks' and try them out without integrating them properly into what we do, they are unlikely to be successful. A tip or trick that someone else recommends likely comes from solving a problem they encountered in their classroom. Ask yourself how, or whether, this also applies in yours. Sarah Cottingham, in her blog *Overpractised*, recommends that when deciding what to change in your practice, start by diagnosing which learning problem you need to work on most. Are your pupils not following instructions? Do your pupils struggle to grasp new concepts? Do your pupils seem to forget everything from last lesson each time? If the tip or trick you want to try out addresses a problem you have and focuses on improving pupils' learning, try it. If not, it might not be the time for that yet. In her own words, *'Changing your teaching without understanding how pupils learn is like setting off on a journey without a map: even if you happen to get there eventually, there was probably a better route.'* (For more on this, listen to Sarah Cottingham on Craig Barton's *Tips for Teachers* podcast: https://tipsforteachers.co.uk/podcast).

Reflective practice

We have mentioned the idea of reflective practice throughout this chapter and elsewhere in the book. Reflection is part of the bedrock of becoming a successful teacher. A reflective practitioner will carve out time to think about what happened in their lessons, mathematically and generally, and look to what actions caused these things to happen. A reflective practitioner accepts that they can change things in their room by changing their own behaviour and is not afraid to work with others to bring about the change they want to see.

A good place to start is to pick something that you thought could have gone better in a lesson and ask yourself questions to think about what happened in more detail. Imagine you realise that your pupils did not understand the main concept of a lesson. You might reflect by asking yourself:

- Did pupils have sufficient prior knowledge to be successful in that lesson? Did I check the prior knowledge of all pupils?

- Did I explain clearly and succinctly? Could I have explained it in another way? Why did I choose that particular approach? Was it the best approach for the pupils or is it the approach I personally prefer?

- Could I have used a different model or representation to help explain the concept better?

- Did I check for understanding of all pupils before giving pupils time to independently practise?

- Did the examples I used support pupils in being successful during the independent practice or was the practice too far removed from them?

- What misconceptions do I need to address next time?

Sometimes you will not know all the answers, and that is okay. Instead of ignoring the problem, look to others for support. You could ask a colleague to observe your next lesson or draw from the advice of others in the department or from your wider networks, or you could record your next lesson, even if it is just the audio, and listen back to your explanations more objectively than your memories of them would be. Some people find the idea of recording themselves daunting, but teachers who do this often cite it as one of the most powerful levers in improving their practice. Classrooms are busy places and a lot can go unnoticed when you are centre stage. Watching or listening to a recording can lead us to seek the solution to a problem we would have been unaware of otherwise.

Sometimes it can be useful to watch someone else teaching. Imagine you decide you want to improve the end of your lessons and shorten the time it takes for your class to pack away. Ask around to find out who has this down to a fine art and go to observe the last ten minutes of their lesson. Be aware that it can be exceedingly difficult to emulate a teacher's practice when routines have become habitual for a class, as it can seem as though things happen like magic; there may be plenty of 'hidden' behaviours that you would not pick up on by watching alone. It is best to watch expert teachers with a new class at the start of the year, so that you can identify how they are training the class in their classroom routines and see the work that is required to embed habits. Take note of what the teacher says and how they say it, how they monitor the pupils' responses and how they respond to them. Talk to the teacher afterwards to help you identify their hidden behaviours – the ones you might not have seen.

Evidence-informed teaching

Teaching, as we have seen, is a complex craft based upon a teacher's knowledge of a subject, subject-specific pedagogy, and general pedagogy. Over the course of recent years, the teaching community's collective knowledge has become increasingly based in evidence and research, so it is essential that we keep ourselves abreast of tested theory and how it might work in the classroom. Dylan Wiliam (2019) says, *'Classrooms are just too complicated for research ever to tell teachers what to do.'* Often the research in psychology and neuroscience contains experimental designs that have taken place in vastly different environments, quietening many of the conditions we contend with in our classrooms; this makes it difficult to simply lift the evidence and implement it into our everyday practice. This does not mean, however, that we should ignore what comes from experimental research, rather we should build our expertise so that we can make better informed judgements about when and how to use the research available to us, promoting an evidence-informed approach to teaching.

Research on learning should be thought of, not as a prescription, but as a compass, providing principles, ideas and heuristics that we can take and translate into our classroom practice (again, for more on this, listen to Sarah Cottingham on Craig Barton's *Tips for Teachers* podcast). When we try to translate any research into the classroom, we should be mindful that we carefully consider the 'active ingredients' of what made the technique a success in the research and keep the fundamental features of this in our implementation. Without this attention, we risk mutating the technique and implementing something that has minimal positive effect or, even worse, a negative effect.

As an example, let us consider retrieval practice. Retrieval practice is any strategy that involves pupils retrieving material that they have previously learned from their long-term memory. Imagine a school that tries to implement retrieval practice as a compulsory 'retrieval starter' in every lesson consisting of four questions on the theme of last lesson/last week/last month/ last year. On the surface, this looks like a valid implementation of the idea of retrieval practice, but the format – which is easily observable – has taken precedence over the substance. Starters take 20 minutes or more, as pupils work on things they haven't seen in a long time and may not be directly related to the learning sequence at hand, and teachers have to take lesson time going through the things the pupils have forgotten. Pupils talk about the questions in this section of the lesson, reducing the effect of 'retrieving' from memory and, in its worse version, the time in lesson for learning new material is reduced to little more than half an hour, with pupils watching the teacher going through something they've forgotten only to repeat the process again the next lesson with a new set of questions. Much better would be to start the lesson with a short task that primes the pupils for today's learning – something that helps them to 'retrieve' prerequisite knowledge, especially if they have also been set homework on this prerequisite knowledge leading up to the lesson. The whole activity, including checking, takes no more than ten minutes, gives relevant and appropriate practice to make for a coherent lesson, and leaves plenty of time for the main substance of the lesson. This kind of 'retrieval starter' may not follow the same format each lesson, but it will be more effective than the former example.

Take time to engage in learning from research but be a 'critical consumer'. Pay attention to the specific features of the research that seem to be effective. If you want to implement a research-based idea, make sure you understand these features so that your implementation doesn't go against them. Check for sample size – an idea tested on ten pupils is not robustly evidenced and effects could be down to chance; one tested on several hundred pupils is more likely to be robustly evidenced, and check for contrary evidence or counterarguments. A great place to start with mathematics-specific research is to sign up to Cambridge Mathematics' *Espressos* newsletter, where research in mathematics cognition and teaching is distilled for busy teachers.

A non-exhaustive list of sources of professional development

Paid memberships

There are two learned societies for teachers of mathematics, both of whom release their own professional journals, provide professional development and publish books you can buy at a discounted rate.

- The Mathematical Association (MA) allows you to develop your mathematical knowledge and offers you the opportunity to network with like-minded individuals, with their wide choice of memberships catering for various levels, from trainees up to institutional memberships. Membership includes free professional development resources and webinars, exclusive online resources, your choice of journal, and monthly and termly newsletters.

- The Association of Teachers of Mathematics (ATM) supports their members with professional support and enrichment. Membership includes the *Mathematics Teaching* journal and access to their online back catalogue of articles and interactive resource links.

Face-to-face courses

- The Advanced Mathematics Support Programme (AMSP) has a range of long-term courses, including those for teaching A Level mathematics, where you can receive bespoke feedback on your lessons and assignments. They also offer face-to-face courses, day courses on topics such as teaching higher attaining pupils and teaching problem-solving.

- The National Centre for Excellence in the Teaching of Mathematics (NCETM) coordinates a wide variety of projects and workshops, most of which are fully funded. Contact your local Maths Hub to see what they have to offer. Courses include subject knowledge enhancement for non-specialists teaching mathematics, the *Teaching for Mastery* programme and the *School Development Lead* programme.

Online courses

- The AMSP have lots of online courses available, live and on demand, giving you the flexibility to access the course at a time that suits you best. Many of these are free or funded.

- You can pay a yearly subscription with Complete Maths to access fantastic online courses in everything from primary mathematics to A Level. A subscription comes with recordings from online conferences and online 'teach meets', where you can discuss various topics with educators across the UK and beyond.

Paid conferences

- ResearchEd conferences feature presentations from educators and researchers in the field and take place throughout the year around the country. There is lots on general teaching ideas, but some have subject-specific strands as well.

- Complete Maths delivers MathsConfs throughout the year around the country and online.

- The mathematics subject associations deliver a conference in Easter, offering high-quality professional development with great networking opportunities. White Rose Maths deliver face-to-face and online conferences, with workshops delivered by their specialists accompanied by inspiring keynote speakers.

- Mathematics Education Innovation (MEI) holds an annual two-day conference in the summer term, with around 50 sessions to choose from, an exhibition, entertainment and, importantly, plenty of opportunities to catch up with other teachers.

Free CPD in your living room

No one expects you to spend your Saturdays travelling to get professional development if you do not want to. Home life is precious, and everyone has different demands outside of school. However, it is still possible to access plenty of brilliant professional development from the comfort of your own home (and with unlimited access to tea).

- **Podcasts:** Great for anyone with a long commute, in the gym, doing the ironing…

  Mathematics-specific:
  - Craig Barton with the *Mr Barton Maths Podcast* and *Tips for Teachers*
  - Kieran Mackle with *Thinking Deeply about Primary Mathematics*
  - Ollie Lovell with *Education Research Reading Room*
  - The NCETM podcast
  - Complete Maths, Dave Taylor with *Teaching Together*

  General:
  - Phil Naylor with *Naylor's Natter*
  - Tom Sherrington and Emma Turner with *Mind the Gap*
  - Arthur Moore and Mike Harrowell's *T and Teaching*
  - Education Endowment Foundation (EEF) Podcasts

- **Blogs:** Great for a quick read…

  Mathematics-specific:
  - Anne Watson and John Mason at pmtheta.com
  - Jo Morgan at resourceaholic.com

○ Dan Draper at mrdrapermathematics.wordpress.com
○ Paul Rowlandson at
  ponderingplanning.wordpress.com
○ Mark McCourt at emaths.co.uk

General:
○ Adam Boxer at achemicalorthodoxy.wordpress.com
○ Sarah Cottingham with overpractised.wordpress.com
○ David Didau with thelearningspy.co.uk

● **Twitter:** The mathematics Twitter community is
  fantastic, and we have learnt so much from it. You have
  the option of being a silent follower, bookmarking any
  interesting ideas or resources that come across your
  feed, or you can use it as a platform to share your
  thoughts and ideas and discuss others' with them.
  The community allows you to widen your network
  outside your department and gives you the opportunity
  to discuss topics with like-minded individuals or with
  those that might disagree or challenge your thinking.

Chapter Summary

In this chapter we have recommended many possible avenues for you to continue to develop as an educator. It is by no means an exhaustive list, but we have tried to include something in here for everyone. It may feel overwhelming with so many great things on offer with a finite amount of time, but this is designed for you to pick up at times that best suit you.

To summarise,

- General pedagogical knowledge, mathematics subject knowledge and mathematics specific pedagogical knowledge are different but equally important to develop to improve teacher quality.
- No one is the finished product; we can always improve.
- It is okay to not know all the answers. Learn from others in your school and the wider mathematics community.

9

Understanding curriculum and assessment

We have taken time over the last few chapters to look at our classroom and our development as a teacher. At this point it would be useful to pause and to take a step up, thinking about a bird's eye view of all the classrooms in our department, and all the year groups in our school.

For any pupil who has learnt maths in our department, their final outcomes – their mathematical knowledge, their perception of the subject and, of course, their exam grades – are the result of every mathematical experience they have had. Every teacher, every period of instruction, every homework set, have all contributed to this final picture. Do our pupils succeed in their exams? Do they enjoy mathematics? Do they place value on mathematics? Do they leave us with a strong, flexible knowledge of mathematics that affords them access to future study in the subject? The answers to these questions compel us to reflect on our *collective* practice as well as our individual practice. This is where the curriculum in our schools comes into focus.

The curriculum is the collection of mathematical experiences that we provide for our pupils. These experiences take many forms: the order in which we sequence content, the methods or procedures that we choose to teach, the explanations that we offer, the types of activity we provide (every task we set, every discussion we coordinate), the ways in which we help pupils to retain their knowledge, the assessment models we use, and the enrichment we provide.

Sequencing and narrative

The mathematics curriculum in England is almost unique amongst subjects in that the content is clearly prescribed (DfE, 2021). The content is split into six (overlapping) strands – Number; Algebra; Ratio, proportion and rates of change; Geometry and measures; Probability; and Statistics – and is statutory. The level of prescription, however, ends there. Decisions must be made by individual schools on how to sequence this content. Some of our sequencing decisions are inevitable. No one would attempt to teach the expansion of two binomials such as $(x+2)(x-3)$ before pupils can multiply with negative numbers and in this respect, much of mathematical knowledge is hierarchical, with many concepts being prerequisite to others. In contrast, some of our sequencing decisions are arbitrary. It doesn't matter whether you teach standard form before scatter graphs, because the ability to work with 4×10^{12} has no bearing on analysis of correlations. In the middle, there are many, many more sequencing decisions that require careful consideration.

In Chapter 1, we met the work of Leslie Dieteker (2015), a professor of mathematics education at Boston University, who created a framework for thinking about the mathematics curriculum as a story, and discussed the benefits of thinking about the narrative that your curriculum tells. To illustrate this idea, we will consider three 'topics' that might be separate on a scheme of work:

   A. Calculations with decimals

   B. Calculations with fractions

   C. Area of quadrilaterals

Let's assume our scheme of work orders these topics A–B–C. What narrative might this ordering tell? Pupils will learn how to extend their knowledge of calculations with positive integers into the realm of decimals. They might learn that multiplying by a number between 0 and 1 gives an answer smaller than the starting number, along with the converse for division. They might focus on the idea that multiplying by 0.1 is equivalent to dividing by 10, and vice versa. Moving to fractions, they will probably abandon familiar column methods and instead learn about common denominators.

The teacher paying attention to narrative will look for ways to link both topics, so they might remind pupils of the '÷ 0.1 is the same as × 10' relation and rewrite it as '÷ $\frac{1}{10}$ is the same as × 10' before linking it to '÷ $\frac{1}{2}$ is the same as × 2', or '÷ $\frac{1}{3}$ is the same as × 3', or '÷ $\frac{3}{5}$ is the same as × $\frac{5}{3}$' through to 'dividing is the same as multiplying by the reciprocal'. When they get to the topic on area of quadrilaterals, they will know that they can set tasks where side lengths are decimals or fractions as a way of practising old learning in the context of new. Since decimal calculations has been known the longest, this topic has had more opportunity for practice and, therefore, might be the most fluent for pupils.

But what happens if we change the sequence? How might the story change? Perhaps we go B–A–C. Now pupils will learn the calculations with fractions first, so they could view the decimal calculations through that lens. The teacher could tell them that, in order to multiply 0.3 and 0.4, they could instead multiply $\frac{3}{10}$ and $\frac{4}{10}$, a connection which would not have been possible in the first ordering. This time, fraction calculations are given some kind of priority as a lens for viewing other calculations and both types of calculations can still be applied in the practice of area.

If the order goes C–A–B or C–B–A, the teacher can no longer use decimals and fractions in their questions on area, unless they include area questions when teaching topics A and B. In this case, the focus shifts subtly – area becomes a means of rehearsing the new learning on calculations with non-integers, rather than the calculations being a means of rehearsing the new learning on area.

Not one of these orders is superior to the others, rather they each come with implications for the pupil's schema. Those topics taught earlier and incorporated into others are likely to be stronger by virtue of having been practised more. Different sequences place greater or less emphasis on different topics. Understanding this is key to deciding how to sequence content not only at the topic-on-a-scheme-of-work level, but also at the level of ordering tasks within a topic.

To illustrate the latter we will use the example from Dieteker's paper. Take the following three tasks from a topic on quadratic graphs and equations (try them before reading on):

A. *Find the roots of* $y = x^2 - 6x + 3$ *by factorising.*

B. *Justin says that* $x^2 - 6x + 3$ *can be rewritten as* $(x - 3)^2 - 6$. *Do you agree? If so, how can you use the expression* $(x - 3)^2 - 6$ *to find the roots of* $y = x^2 - 6x + 3$?

C. *Graph* $y = x^2 - 6x + 3$ *and estimate the x-intercepts, if any.*

If we order these A–B–C, pupils will try (and probably fail) to factorise in A, perhaps concluding that there are no roots. They will proceed to complete the square in B, solve for $y = 0$ and discover that there are in fact two irrational roots, so their initial conclusion was wrong. Moving onto C gives them a third, potentially redundant method of finding the roots.

A change in order changes the narrative. If we proceed A–C–B, pupils fail to factorise as before, but now the drawing of the graph exposes the wrong conclusion and motivates the need for another method, ushering in B. Dieteker suggests that this order creates 'suspense' in the narrative. Take a moment to think about other orderings of the tasks and how they change the story.

To reiterate, no one order is always superior to the others, but we must understand that how we sequence content tells a story which shapes how our pupils make sense of mathematics.

Another practical aspect of sequencing is the timing given to units of work. In England, schemes of work that allow only a handful of lessons on a topic before 'moving on' are commonplace. In the light of our discussion in Chapter 7 on the Björks' New Theory of Disuse, this approach is risky. If time is not properly allotted to learn something in depth, its storage strength will be low, it is likely to be forgotten and will need reteaching. If, instead, longer periods of time allow for more practice and more exploration of a topic, storage strength is likely to be higher so subsequent activities can be designed with retrieval strength in mind.

Increasing the length of units of work allows for 'overlearning'. The 1982 Cockcroft Report into mathematics teaching in England highlighted the importance of practice that allows pupils to commit a procedure to memory, stating that 'well-mastered routines are necessary in order to free conscious attention as much as possible so that it can focus on aspects of a task which are novel or problematic'. The report anticipated what has been later evidenced in cognitive science, that when pupils have time to practise to a point of overlearning – the principle summed up by the adage 'don't practise till you get it right; practise until you can't get it wrong' – their working memory is freed up to think about applying the mathematics to solving problems (there is a bigger discussion of this in Chapter 7).

It is not unusual to worry that taking an approach that allows more time for initial learning will cause us to run out of time to cover the entire National Curriculum. If done well, however, this concern falls away. In-depth initial learning should be accompanied by regular retrieval practice in various forms, including the deliberate assimilation of old learning into new. When finding area, for instance, pupils can work with decimal and fractional lengths to practise these calculations anew. When solving quadratics, pupils can manipulate answers in surd form to remind them of rationalising and simplifying. The nature of mathematics allows for this assimilation almost everywhere, and we should actively look for opportunities to exploit it (for an interesting take on this, look at Nathan Day's *Interwoven Maths* at https://interwovenmaths.com). Such an approach gives little need to reteach (from scratch) and, combined with the principles of coherence, allows pupils to create a connected schema, developing both their procedural and conceptual understanding (see Chapter 5). Teaching this way – deep initial learning, plenty of quality practice, a coherent curriculum model, assimilating old topics into new, and regular retrieval practice from then on – reduces the need for complete reteaching. As a consequence, there is still time to teach the whole National Curriculum well.

Coherence

Our bird's eye view of curriculum leads us to think about coherence. The Cambridge English Dictionary defines 'coherence' as *'the situation when the parts of something fit together in a natural or reasonable way'* or *'a clear relationship between parts'*. A curriculum is coherent if all its parts fit together to form a logical, consistent whole, much like a novel is coherent when all the parts fit together to tell a story.

It can be helpful to think about coherence by considering to what extent our curriculum is held together by threads. There are different types of threads that can contribute to a coherent curriculum and we will focus on three important ones: concepts, methods and representations.

Concept threads

Mathematics is all about concepts. Multiplication, addition, proportionality and equality are all examples of concepts that thread throughout our subject, and any procedures we perform are always in service to an underlying concept. In Chapter 5 we looked at how the concept of multiplication is deepened over time, going from arrays and the multiplication tables right up to completing the square or polynomial division. The power of thinking about concepts in terms of threads is in the coherence it creates. If, whenever we talk about multiplication, we present it in a familiar way, pupils will be less likely to see all these manifestations as entirely different things. Do your pupils know that $2(3x + 1)$ is barely different to 2×31? If so, you are likely threading multiplication through your curriculum in a coherent way (and we will discuss practical ways of doing this throughout this chapter).

An 'addition thread' might look like this:

Addition through the curriculum	• Addition with positive integers, using the ideas of 'exchange' and 'likeness' in algorithms. • Addition with positive decimals, using the ideas of 'exchange' and 'likeness' in algorithms. • Addition with fractions, using the ideas of 'exchange' and 'likeness' in common denominators. • Addition with negative numbers, using previous methods but including the idea of 'zero pair'. • Addition with algebraic expressions, using the ideas of 'likeness' in like terms and 'zero pair'.

The ideas of 'exchange' and 'likeness' are fundamental to addition. When we add, for instance, 26 and 37 in a column, we start with the ones – those digits that are 'like' in their place value. 6 ones and 7 ones and get 13 ones. The 3 stays in the ones column but we 'exchange' the ten ones for one ten and move this to the tens column, to be added to the 2 tens and 3 tens in 26 and 37, again only adding the digits that are 'like'.

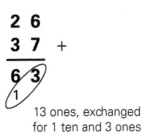

13 ones, exchanged
for 1 ten and 3 ones

The same thing happens with decimals, and the connection to integers is generally clear by virtue of using the same column algorithm (if that is the one chosen). In contrast, adding fractions can seem completely different, something new to learn that is not like any adding seen before. Greater scrutiny of the process, however, reveals the same ideas. If we are to add $\frac{2}{3}$ and $\frac{1}{6}$, we recognise that thirds are not 'like' sixths, so we 'exchange' $\frac{2}{3}$ for $\frac{4}{6}$ so that we can add 'like' numbers. The presentation may be different, but the mathematics is not. We can see how the idea of 'likeness' extends to algebraic expressions, where we 'simplify' $2x + 5y + x + 10y$ by adding the like terms to get $3x + 15y$. Different presentation, same mathematics.

By analysing our curriculum in terms of concept threads and looking at where concepts arise again and again, we can engineer our classroom instruction to exploit these threads, making explicit the links between new learning and old, helping pupils to see mathematics as a connected whole rather than a series of disconnected procedures.

Method threads

Imagine three teachers in a maths department where there is no thought to threading methods. Every teacher chooses their preferred methods and sticks to them. One year, the topic of expanding two binomials is on the scheme of work. Our pupil is in Teacher A's class, where she learns that you expand brackets using the 'smiley face'.

The next year our pupil is going to learn about solving a quadratic equation and is now taught by Teacher B, who always expands brackets with FOIL (first, outer, inner, last).

$$(x - 2)(x + 5)$$

F x^2
O $5x$
I $-2x$
L -10

Our pupil hasn't seen FOIL before (she knows the smiley face) and tells the teacher, who replies, *'Ah, well I do it this way, but it's the same really'* and proceeds with their preference. Moving to year three of working with quadratics, and our pupil is going to sketch the graphs and compare factorising with the quadratic formula and completing the square. This time, she has Teacher C who swears by the grid method.

$\times$	x	5
x	x^2	$5x$
-2	$-2x$	-10

Again, this presentation of the process is totally new to our pupil, who had a year of the smiley face followed by a year of FOIL. What is the effect of this free-for-all on methods? Potentially nothing. Our pupil may have made sense of the process enough to see that all these methods achieve the same aim in precisely the same way, the differences being purely superficial. However, we know from experience that many pupils do not make sense of mathematics enough to see this. It is these pupils who will suffer the most from this incoherent approach.

If instead, the teachers in the department got together and decided on their collective method, those pupils who need coherence to help them make meaning (which is the overwhelming majority) will only benefit. They will be more likely to assimilate the new learning each year if they don't also have to make sense of or remember a new method, since their attention will be focused on the new information added to what they learnt before. Teacher preference is not a good basis for selection of methods if that preference creates incoherence or an artificial obstacle for pupils to overcome.

Methods threaded through a curriculum contribute to the understanding of concepts. Let's take the grid method for multiplication as an example. The grid method exposes the axiom of *distributivity* particularly well. For multiplying integers it looks like this.

$$350 \times 12 = 4200$$

×	10	2
300	3000	600
50	500	100

The same works for decimals.

$$3.5 \times 1.2 = 4.2$$

×	1	0.2
3	3	0.6
0.5	0.5	0.1

And even for fractions.

$$3\tfrac{1}{2} \times 1\tfrac{1}{5} = 4\tfrac{1}{5}$$

×	1	$\frac{1}{5}$
3	3	$\frac{3}{5}$
$\frac{1}{2}$	$\frac{1}{2}$	$\frac{1}{10}$

If we are to multiply linear expressions, it still works:

$$(3x + 5)(x + 2) = 3x^2 + 11x + 10$$

×	x	2
3x	$3x^2$	6x
5	5x	10

As it does for non-linear expressions and those with more than two terms, like this:

$\times$	x	$2y$	7
x^3	x^4	$2x^3y$	$7x^3$
1	x	$2y$	7

And even for polynomial division, working in reverse. The key is that all these 'topics' are part of the same concept, that of multiplication, and by keeping a consistent method we thread the topics together, helping pupils to see these links.

Representation threads

In Chapter 4, we looked at representations, exploring how the more abstract symbolic representation of algebra (that is, using letters to represent variables and unknowns) can be evasive for some pupils but becomes more readily accessed when we also approach concepts through concrete and pictorial representations at the same time. It is important to reiterate here that the concrete, the pictorial and the symbolic are all representations of concepts, means of sense-making in the abstract. Symbolic representations (numbers, letters, operators) are used most often because they provide the most succinct and transferable way we have of thinking about abstract concepts, but they are not the only way. By recognising the power of concrete and pictorial representations, and by knowing that this power is increased as such representations become familiar to pupils, we have another thread to help us build coherence in a curriculum.

As our exemplar, refer back to the example of the number line and double number line in Chapter 4. Young pupils become familiar with the number line for natural numbers from the earliest years of schooling. This line is extended to fractions and decimals (rational numbers) in primary school and to negative numbers at the end of primary and start of secondary. Once pupils understand the number line, we can introduce the double number line as a way of representing proportional reasoning.

When thinking proportionally, we know that two sets of quantities are linked by a multiplicative relationship: if one is doubled, so is the other; if one is zero, so is the other. Scenarios such as currency conversions, price of goods, percentages of amounts and compound measures fit this category. A double number line exploits this multiplicative relationship, along with the idea of multiplication producing a stretch, to fit together two number lines representing different quantities related proportionally. The beauty in this representation is that any multiplication (or division) performed horizontally is mirrored on both lines, as is any performed vertically between the lines.

Once pupils are familiar with how to work with double number lines, they can learn to use them to help them think about any proportional relationship, linking together seemingly separate areas of mathematics by exposing their deep structure – that of proportional reasoning – which continues right up to algebraic proportional reasoning in the latter years of compulsory mathematics study.

If used consistently and regularly, the double number line (like any representation) becomes familiar to pupils. With this familiarity comes a recognition of 'what to do' straightaway, the ability to add layers of complexity to the mathematics with relative ease and the deliberate and explicit building of links within topics taught at different times throughout the years. It is these links that encourage flexibility of knowledge, as we discussed in Chapter 5.

Other threads

There are other parts of learning that should be woven into a curriculum. A mathematics team should plan how they are going to gradually develop pupils' fluency and confidence with mathematical language and communication, for instance, so that sophistication increases over time according to a deliberate plan. Enrichment within and outside the classroom should complement the statutory curriculum (see Chapter 6). The development of pupils' awareness of the uses and applications of mathematics, and what doors it opens for them, should be built in at the right times. Competency with mathematical equipment such as compasses, protractors and calculators should be developed over time in the same way that mathematical content knowledge should. As with any other curricular thread, repeated exposure to an idea in increasingly sophisticated ways will always be more effective than a one-off event.

Collective responsibility

At no point in the discussion of coherence are we suggesting that one way of doing things is superior to another. Instead, we are highlighting that a pupil's learning is likely to be greater if every teacher they encounter is working towards the same aim. Back in Chapter 1 we looked at the idea of collaboration, emphasising how a department working towards the same goal, planning activities, tasks and sequences together, is superior to each teacher working in their own silo and only taking responsibility for their own class. Every one of us assimilates new information through the lens of our existing understanding, so every teacher must assume the next step in their pupils' particular journey.

Cast your mind back to a training session you have attended with colleagues and the discussions you had about it afterwards. Everyone in the session will have focused on different aspects, having their attention drawn to the parts that made most sense to them. Someone may have been having similar thoughts already and found reinforcement or validation in parts of it, while someone else heard something that challenged their existing conceptions. Still someone else will have taken very little from the session, because it didn't have any relevance to their existing knowledge. This scenario happens because every one of us interprets the world through the lens of our existing understanding.

The same thing happens in the mathematics classroom and it has implications on what we teach and how we teach it. Teachers in a department must take collective responsibility to continue the journey the pupil is on. If a pupil has learnt an aspect of mathematics a certain way, this will inform how they interpret and make sense of new mathematics that they encounter. If they have learnt multiplication of numbers with a grid method, for instance, then that structure is familiar to them. Using it for multiplication of increasingly complex expressions is likely to be more successful than presenting this mathematics in a different way. A teacher who accepts this may often teach using methods that are not their preferred ones, but they understand that this is inconsequential if they are the ones that best build on pupils' existing knowledge and understanding. Inter-teacher coherence is a feature of a strong curriculum that accepts our collective responsibility for our pupils' learning.

The second implication of us interpreting the world through the lens of our existing understanding is that 'what to teach' is more complex than 'what's on the scheme of work for this week?' It is important that pupils learn the mathematics that they are ready to learn. If they are taught something too far removed from their current understanding, they will struggle to make any meaning. A curriculum model that ploughs on through, regardless of whether or not prereqisite knowledge is secure, is a model that will, by design, fail groups of pupils.

The impetus on the teacher is to teach the right content at the right time, and to use all the diagnostic tools at their disposal to help them ascertain what is the right content and when is the right time. In Chapter 7, we considered this idea through the lens of cognitive load, selecting tasks with the right intrinsic load. Now we extend it through the lens of curriculum.

The structure and implementation of a curriculum must be focused on knowledge acquisition – on pupils simultaneously developing procedural and conceptual knowledge and increasing their depth of understanding – and the collective responsibility of a department is to work out what pupils should learn when and how to teach effectively to increase the chances of success. This compels departmental leadership to implement a responsive scheme of work, one that maps out the coherent journey the department will follow, but which allows for varying speeds of progression through it. A head of department working with a responsive scheme of work will need to use quality assurance to keep an eye on what's happening, making sure that every child is being stretched appropriately and that there are no glass ceilings on low prior attainers or those with SEND. Where issues are found, professional development is key to their resolution. Chapter 8 explored the fundamental role of a team's professional development in making a curriculum model successful. The main tool for finding issues is assessment.

Assessment

There is an old proverb that says, 'a watched pot never boils'. Assessment is not an end in itself; it is only useful when it serves a purpose. In Chapter 3 on responsive teaching, we discussed the purpose of formative assessment in shaping and directing teacher activity and, as a consequence, pupil learning. The purpose of formative assessment is to enable responsiveness, where teachers adapt instruction to pupils' learning on an ongoing basis. In this chapter we will focus on summative assessment, which serves a different end, giving us a broad, high-level snapshot of what pupils have learnt at a specific moment in time. It is important to take this brief discussion of summative assessment alongside Chapter 3 and it will probably be helpful to reread the latter once you have finished this section.

A summative assessment samples all the content pupils have been learning and reports their respective successes in this sample. As such, we must be careful how we create and deploy summative assessments and be even more careful about the conclusions or inferences we draw from them. Before you decide to set summative assessments, and especially before you start creating them, you must decide the purpose of the assessment and firm up how you want to use its results. Is the assessment intended to check how well pupils are learning your curriculum? Will you be reporting results to parents or to senior leaders? Will it contribute to decisions on set changes (which, importantly, should never take place on the basis of a single assessment)? The answers to these questions determine the type and size of the assessment, the information you collect from it and the way you distil that information.

An assessment consisting of well-designed multiple-choice questions, which will expose misconceptions and common mistakes, is great for helping you decide how well classroom teaching is going, especially if it shows up disparities between classrooms, or if it highlights weak areas common to all. If you use the flags that such an assessment raises to dig a little deeper, prompt discussions and professional development, then the assessment served a clear purpose and was designed to meet that purpose. This is likely to be a valid use of this type of assessment.

Trying to use a past GCSE paper for the same purpose (finding out how teaching is going) is likely to lack validity. A GCSE paper is designed to be a differentiator at the very end of a course. It contains a small sample of the learning of the previous five (or more) years, and assesses the sample in increasingly complex ways in order to rank order and assign grades to a large cohort. No amount of question-level analysis (QLA) of a GCSE paper will be diagnostic enough to address gaps in teaching or learning – it is the wrong tool for the job. Daisy Christodoulou highlights the potential problems with inference from QLA in *Making Good Progress?* emphasising that no marks on a multi-step question does not mean the pupils couldn't do the underlying subject content of that question. A 'red' on a QLA spreadsheet doesn't tell us where they slipped up, whether they were thrown by the wording, whether they misread the numbers, whether they typed something in their calculator wrong, or whether they genuinely had no clue about the mathematics. Some broad trends might be observable from a GCSE paper QLA, but a lot of effort goes into them and the resulting inferences may not be valid.

If the purpose of an assessment is to report to parents on their child's progress, then the information reported must be useful to the recipient. Imagine you have set half-termly topic tests that are closely aligned to the taught curriculum. You could use these to let parents know their child's average score across the tests and how this compares to the class or the cohort, giving parents some perspective on how their child is getting on.

If this is your purpose, you need to ensure that your topic tests are reliable indicators of learning. Lots of non-routine problems, for instance, will deflate scores, although a small number of carefully selected problems (alongside routine questions) can check for depth of understanding. Lots of worded questions will disadvantage pupils whose reading level is lower than others, reducing equity of access, where some worded questions (alongside routine questions) can check for method selection. What this highlights to us is that it is practically impossible to make completely reliable assessments. Once we know this, we can use them appropriately, safe in the knowledge of their limitations, but keep an eye on how we can improve them.

One way to evaluate the reliability of your assessments is to look at the distribution of results. Imagine no one in the cohort gets above 60 per cent. What can you infer from this? It could be that all the teaching in the department needs improving (unlikely, but possible). What's more likely is that the test was not a reliable measure of what you've been teaching. In this case, it's not fair to report to parents or school leaders using that test. Next, imagine that the whole cohort achieved over 80 per cent. What can we infer this time? Perhaps everyone's teaching was superb. Perhaps someone got sight of the test and shared it in advance. Perhaps the assessment was too easy and didn't sufficiently test the content with enough rigour. If the latter, the test is unreliable and your inferences from it invalid.

Does this mean that we should always be looking for a test to produce a wide distribution of scores? The answer to that question comes back to purpose. If the purpose of the test is to assess content learnt, a wide distribution is broadly irrelevant – neither helpful nor unhelpful. If the purpose is to report to parents, then an indicator of placement in the cohort (combined with some simple information on weaker areas of learning) can be useful for them to understand what kind of support to give their child. If the purpose of the test is to contribute towards a rank ordering of pupils which is then used to make GCSE predictions, then a distribution as wide as necessary to achieve that aim is helpful, and you will likely want to aggregate a number of assessment results over time rather than just use one.

The salient point here is that all summative assessment takes time from other things in the classroom and puts some kind of value judgement onto a child. As such, an understanding of the purpose of assessment, efforts to make assessments as reliable as possible and a commitment to make only valid inferences from them are imperative. This short section does not explore these issues in nearly enough detail but the suggestions in Further reading will help you to learn more about good practice around assessment.

Chapter Summary

In this chapter we explored the imperative for a whole department creating a coherent mathematics curriculum, particularly thinking about the following.

- The success of any one pupil is dependent upon all the mathematical experiences they have throughout their time with us.
- The sequencing of our curriculum and the learning episodes within it tell a story.
- Concepts, methods and representations should be carefully threaded throughout the curriculum to create coherence.
- We should plan to develop mathematical thinking and communication skills, as well as use of mathematical equipment, over time.
- Summative assessment must have validity and reliability. Be aware of the limitations of any assessment and use assessments with these limitations in mind.

FURTHER READING

Daisy Christodoulou's *Making Good Progress?* (2017) contains a comprehensive discussion of formative and summative assessment, its validity in schools, and how we can get better at assessment.

Teaching for Mastery by Mark McCourt (2019) has the best described exemplars of threading a representation through a curriculum that we have seen to date.

The *Assessment Lead Programme* from Evidence Based Education is invaluable for anyone looking to implement assessments well across a school or a department.

10

Developing your team

Leading a mathematics department is an important role, one which can impact significantly on whole-school outcomes and life chances of pupils. As leaders, our job is not to do *everything* within the department ourselves – such a thing would not be possible – but instead to ensure everything runs well, to simultaneously allow staff to thrive and to hold them accountable, and to take responsibility for the culture of learning in our department. We must remember that the most important thing is what is going on in each classroom, every day, therefore our greatest responsibility is to ensure that we support every member of our team to improve, whatever their starting point. This is far easier to achieve if we get the culture of the department right so that, rather than each teacher working in isolation, the whole team feels that they are working towards and contributing to a common goal. In turn, teacher wellbeing and staff retention are high if teachers feel valued and supported. Creating the right culture in our teams is too important to leave to chance.

In her book *High Challenge, Low Threat* (2016), Mary Myatt talks about how a great many small actions can fit together to establish a culture where teachers feel secure and happy but are challenged to constantly improve. Adam Boxer discusses the importance of making the culture of a department explicit, as a means to lowering workload and building a better team ethic (https://tipsforteachers.co.uk/cult ure). Boxer advocates being clear about what we are doing and why we are doing it, and showing accountability when we fail to meet the mark. Meanwhile, Sam Crome (2022a) explains that improved teamwork can lead to improved cohesion, wellbeing, performance and job satisfaction. The fact is that everyone in the department has a key part to play in its overall effectiveness and performance, even though school performance management measures can often overlook this. While a lot of focus can end up on year 11 borderline groups, or certain pupil demographics, no intervention will ever be better than excellent teaching throughout the school.

Team culture

Our moral purpose should underpin everything that we do and should be communicated to our team regularly and with clarity. In defining our moral purpose, we set our team's common ground and motivation. Everything we do should be linked to that moral purpose and should benefit the team, the pupils or individual teachers.

Authenticity is a fundamental aspect of leadership. If everyone knows that we have the right motivations at the heart of what we do, it makes it far easier to work with us and feel proud to be part of the team. In *How to be an Amazing Middle Leader* (2014), Caroline Bentley-Davies notes that it is more satisfying to work with a leader who genuinely has the best interests of pupils and staff at heart than someone who is only interested in making themselves look good. Authenticity includes honesty and owning our mistakes. In trying things, it is inevitable that mistakes will happen and there will be times when we must apologise to our teams for getting something wrong. It is far better to be humble and admit that we have made a mistake than to try to pretend that we are perfect. As well as showing that we are genuine, we are also modelling to others in the team how they should approach having made a mistake, by addressing it quickly and learning from it. Certainly when someone else in our team has made a mistake, we would far rather hear about it quickly from them, than further down the line from someone else when it may have gone too far to be remedied.

Fundamentally, building a team is about developing productive professional relationships with and between its members. Relationships take time to establish and maintain. They require an investment from us, in an environment where we often feel that there is not enough time for all the demands upon us. However, this investment is the core role of a department leader. By investing time in our team, we understand their strengths, weaknesses and aspirations, and we show them that they are valued and appreciated. Set and protect time to communicate with your team and for them to work together. The best leaders make sure they check in regularly with each member of their team with brief, personal interactions, building up what Myatt calls a *'bank balance of goodwill'*, keeping an eye on everyone's health and wellbeing, and increasing our availability to those we lead. Bentley-Davies highlights the importance of leaders being approachable and available, to discuss ideas and issues with, on an informal basis as much as in designated meetings. For instance, we might want to seek a teacher's opinion on something prior to discussing it with the rest of the team, showing that we value their opinion and trust their judgement. There is as much power in small chats as in large conversations, both in keeping an overview of the team and in building the culture we aim for.

Having 'skin in the game'

In *Middle Leadership* Mastery (2021), Adam Robbins discusses the importance of authenticity – of leaders having *'skin in the game'* – showing that they get stuck in and that they can walk the walk as well as talk the talk. Leaders must make sure that they follow through on anything they are asking the rest of the department to do. Trust is paramount, and we must do what we say we are going to do. There are many ways that leaders can show that they are willing to step up and do whatever is needed, from tackling behavioural issues on the corridors, to ensuring that they take their fair share of tough classes. Such actions are far more likely to garner respect and buy-in from the rest of the team than a leader who stays in their classroom or office while chaos reigns outside, or who makes sure that they always teach the top sets. There is no point in telling a department, *'we are all in this together'* if our actions say the opposite.

A culture of openness and safety

A key role of a leader is to quality-assure the work of their team. In a school context, lesson observations, learning walks and book scrutiny form the backbone of this. People rarely like to feel under scrutiny, and most teachers do not relish the prospect of somebody coming in to observe their teaching or look at the books of their classes, especially if these activities result in personal judgements. However, the processes of quality assurance are crucial if we are to create a culture of improvement with its associated checks and balances.

What if we were able to develop a culture within our team where teachers welcomed rather than feared others coming to see them teach? What if our teachers were keen to discuss with us and each other what they are seeking to improve and how they might go about it? People almost always come to work wanting to do a good job and wanting to get better and learn more. The processes of quality assurance are a key lever for staff development, which become even more powerful in a culture of openness to feedback and improvement, combined with staff knowing that they are safe and not being judged in the process. Let us consider some steps we can take that could begin to foster this.

Firstly, we need to take responsibility for leading this culture in our teams by making it clear that every single one of us has things we can improve in our teaching. Dylan Wiliam (2012) makes this point very powerfully when he says that as teachers, we fail every single day; in fact, *'if you're not failing on a daily basis then you're just not paying attention'*. Every one of us can learn from our experiences and hone or refine what we do, and making it clear that we are improving our own teaching sets the precedent for everyone else in the team. In talking about our own process of self-reflection, we show that we too are fallible and that transparency around development is a good thing. In doing so we model to the rest of the team behaviours we want to see from them.

We need to have a good understanding of the strengths, areas to develop and aspirations of each member of our team, built up from a combination of our daily interactions with them and seeing them teach. We may have aspirations for them ourselves, such as identifying that they have great leadership potential even before they can see it. It should be noted, however, that not all teachers want to go on to be leaders themselves, preferring instead to hone their craft and be the most thoroughly excellent classroom practitioner they can be, and such teachers should be highly valued and cherished. We must create the conditions for each person to be able to improve and flourish with a mixture of guidance, coaching and relevant CPD opportunities. A good head of department will build their team to compensate for aspects of the job they are weaker at, but will read widely to build their own skills and to know how best to train their department.

To create an environment where observation is seen as developmental and not judgemental, we should start by inviting the team to watch *us* teach. This demonstrates openness and transparency and an opportunity for humility: which of my actions had a positive effect on the lesson? What opportunities did I miss? Both the lesson and conversations arising from it set an example to the rest of the team on behaviours you want to see from them. Some departments have an open-door culture where they are happy for colleagues to watch them teach at any time. An environment of psychological safety is essential here, where there is a shared feeling of safety to take risks without fear of backlash. Sam Crome (2022b) describes psychologically safe teams as having a culture of openness and curiosity, built through constructive feedback, the freedom to fail, and leaders having the humility to admit when they do not know something. The freedom to fail comes when teachers know that mistakes won't be used to judge them 'officially', and that improvement is iterative and comes with practice.

Collective departmental development time is a key feature of improvement for all and can be a cornerstone of culture development. In this time, a leader can share key messages about departmental priorities and why they matter, making sure everyone is able to pull in the same direction. Use the members of your team actively in professional development time. If someone is an expert in a topic or pedagogical approach, ask them to lead the session. Wherever possible, keep admin to email and separate from professional development time, so that these sessions focus on the right thing: time for the team to think about, discuss and do maths together. Open discussions about different methods and approaches, and working together to build coherence between years and classrooms, is time well spent (the NCETM blog (2022) gives an example of how one department utilises collaborative planning). Once habitual, these conversations tend to continue informally outside of meetings, leading to greater collegiality and a greater depth of knowledge across the team.

Non-specialists in the mathematics team

Our culture of openness and safety must extend to everyone who teaches mathematics in our department, and this can often include teachers we might term 'non-specialist'.

What does 'specialism' look like in mathematics teaching? There are many paths into maths teaching and the labels 'specialist' and 'non-specialist' fail to capture the makeup of a someone's mathematical background. Consider the examples below. Which of these teachers would you consider 'specialist' and which 'non-specialist'?

- A teacher who studied a history degree, then completed a post-graduate teaching qualification in history but began teaching maths during their first year of teaching and has taught solely maths for the last 20 years, up to and including A Level.

- A teacher who studied a law degree, then completed a post-graduate teaching qualification in maths including a subject-knowledge enhancement year, and has taught maths ever since.

- A business studies teacher who had been teaching for ten years before they undertook a maths conversion course and has taught both business studies and maths for the last four years.

● A maths graduate who has just started an initial teacher training course.

There is clearly a spectrum of specialism. In fact, there is a spectrum of specialism in mathematics subject knowledge and a separate (but related one) in mathematics-specific pedagogical knowledge. The last teacher in the list above will have good mathematics knowledge but practically no knowledge of how to teach maths, whereas the first is likely to be skilled in communicating school-level mathematics despite not having studied it to the same level in their earlier years. Understanding where staff in your department sit on both spectra can help you to identify where professional development can best be targeted. Those who have not completed a post-graduate teaching qualification in mathematics tend to be called 'non-specialists' but these people do not form a homogenous group, as the examples above highlight.

Changes to the content of maths GCSE from September 2015 included introducing some topics never before assessed at GCSE. In the context of non-specialist staff, you may find that there are topics they have to teach that they have never been taught themselves. The 2018 Nuffield Report looking at maths teacher allocations noted that *inexperienced and out-of-subject maths teachers are much more likely to be allocated to Key Stage 3 than Key Stages 4 or 5'* and that *'teachers with no post-compulsory qualifications in maths were more likely to be allocated to low-ability sets'* (Allen and Sims, 2018, p. 10). Although such decisions about teacher allocation are understandable, we have to ensure that non-specialists are properly supported so that the quality of teaching at Key Stage 3 remains high, that pupils attitudes to mathematics remain positive, and that they are well prepared for their next steps. There are courses available for teachers of other subjects to retrain as maths teachers (NCETM, n.d.) and these are an important first step in the process of retraining (Sani and Burghes, 2021). Ongoing development, through joining in the departmental collaboration we discussed earlier in the chapter, is essential for helping these teachers to gain a deeper understanding of mathematics-specific pedagogy. Although sometimes challenging if they teach multiple subject areas, it is vital that non-specialists are included in any departmental professional development time and are given ample opportunities to work collaboratively with the rest of the team.

Watching lessons, giving feedback and coaching staff

Observing lessons is a standard part of quality assurance. Spending time seeing your team teach helps you to get a good picture of the mathematical experiences your pupils get, how these change from classroom to classroom, and where teacher's expertise is strong or needs developing. There is no better way to gauge this than to see people teach. There are, however, some extremely important principles to be aware of before going into anyone else's classroom.

Time spent in lessons is as much to watch the pupils as it is teachers. Make sure pupils know that you will always support your staff and reinforce high expectations of behaviour and learning. A head of department who is seen around and about, who fills their team with confidence that they will support them to do their job well, and who models to the pupils how things work in the mathematics department, is a head of department who is proactively creating a positive culture.

No one likes to be judged. Observations that place too much emphasis on evaluating their teachers place too much weight on the validity of a snapshot. An individual lesson should never be graded – there is too much variance from observers for this to be effective. The Measures of Effective Teaching Project found that if a lesson is judged 'Outstanding' by one mentor/observer, the probability that a second person would give a different judgement is between 51% and 78%. Instead, time spent in lessons should be genuinely developmental and should be part of a dialogue. If you go in, tell someone what they must do to improve and disappear again, then you are working against a culture of openness and safety. There will be thousands of teacher and pupil behaviours you don't notice and the person you are watching will, inevitably, not make the same decisions you might have done were you at the front. Talk to people about what they did, and why, and never make sweeping judgements on anyone based on a short time in their classroom.

If you do spend time in lessons and realise that you wish to develop an aspect of a colleague's practice, it is important to understand how improvement happens. Habits are often unconscious and always, by definition, embedded. Telling someone to work on something is rarely enough to make a strong, sustained change, and telling someone lots of things in one go is overloading and will reduce the chance of any one thing being acted upon – cognitive load theory applies to adults as well as children! To improve an aspect of their practice, a teacher first needs to see the good practice in action to get a mental model of what they are aiming for. They then need time to rehearse the new behaviours themselves until they become a normal part of what they do, and they must have feedback along the way to make sure they are on track. If you have created a culture of safety and openness in your department, staff will be happy to take part in processes like this. If staff feel judged or 'under fire', then you need to work on your departmental culture first. Instructional coaching is a great model for maintaining sustained improvements, taking into account what we know about how people get better at things.

To be developmental, feedback should focus on the specifics of practice that were effective, not on a teacher's personality and not on generic statements. Compare, *'You are so great at teaching geometric proof!'* with, *'It was effective how you started with a goal-free problem. I noticed that this encouraged pupils to start by considering everything they knew from the given information, without worrying about the end result.'* The first comment is vague and focused on the teacher, the latter is focused on how the actions of the teacher improved pupils' learning. Feedback should be about the teaching, not the teacher.

Not all feedback on teaching (rather than teachers) is of equal quality. A novice teacher might be told they need to 'increase the pace' of their lessons when the observer notices too many pupils not paying much attention. Without any indication of precisely how to do this, they could reasonably conclude that they need to talk quicker or give pupils less independent practice. We should give a teacher the tools and guidance they need to make genuine improvements in their practice. In contrast to an instruction to increase pace, you might say the following: *'There are periods of time in your lesson when most of the pupils in the room are not having to think hard about what you are teaching them. I would like you to practise giving an uninterrupted explanation of the process and then use the mini-whiteboards to make every pupil practise the process and allow you to check they understood it. Try and keep this to around five minutes in your next lesson.'*

Teacher improvement is little different from the process of pupils learning more – feedback should be pitched where a teacher's level of expertise currently is and be designed to move them on, much in the way our teaching of pupils must meet them where their current knowledge is and move them on.

A teacher's level of expertise is a critical factor in determining what information is relevant for them and what information they will attend to. Knowing your team and their expertise is essential. When someone is more novice, you will need to provide them with explicit guidance. As they become more expert, it can be better to ask probing questions to facilitate development. Remember that everyone is more novice at some things and more expert at others – learn your team.

An example of an action step for precise feedback

It is the start of the new academic year and Ben has instructed his class to begin an independent task in silence. Most of the pupils initially do this. Three pupils have not started and are whispering about their plans for after school. Ben does not scan the room to check for compliance. Instead, he immediately begins to help a pupil who has raised their hand. He crouches down to get to the same height as the pupil. The off-task pupils continue to chat without consequence. Other pupils notice the non-compliance going unchecked, so they begin to talk too. This noise level continues to rise until Ben can no longer hear the pupil he is trying to help. He stands, using a formal posture – squaring his shoulders and standing still – to address the whole class, 'Year 10, I asked for silence, and this is NOT silence.' He pauses and waits for the class to be silent, before returning to the pupil who needed help.

After observing this snapshot of the lesson, the observer comments to Ben, 'Keep all pupils on task.'

As feedback, this is incredibly vague, giving nothing concrete for the teacher to work with. If Ben knew how to do this already, he probably would have done it in that lesson.

A better action step would be, 'When you set pupils off on any independent work, stand in the corner of the room

> *for 1–2 minutes, so that you can see all pupils. Monitor their compliance by making it obvious you are looking around, seeing all areas of the room.'*
>
> *Ben now has something specific he can practise from his very next lesson.*

Shared language

Developing a shared language of techniques in a department or school allows conversations to run at a much quicker pace with a better understanding of what is required. With time, you do not need to give the detail of that technique – you can simply refer to it with its codified name during a conversation, with both parties still being aware of all the finer details that go along with it. A lot of schools use shared language and share it with their pupils too, so you might be aware of some frequently used vocabulary. The action step given to Ben in the case study referred to standing in the corner of the room to see everyone, to monitor compliance, and to make it obvious to the pupils that you are watching. In Doug Lemov's *Teach Like a Champion* (2021), this position is referred to as *'Pastore's Perch'*, named after a teacher Lemov observed doing this to great effect. If everyone in the department knows the name of the position, we can simply say, *'As you set pupils off on independent practice, move to Pastore's Perch,'* and in doing so we streamline our communication and can be confident that everyone understands what we mean. This is the same principle as teaching academic vocabulary to our pupils – it allows them (and, in this case, us) to converse in an efficient, accurate and mutually understood way.

Shared language does not need to be taken from *Teach Like a Champion*, but it is a brilliant tool to use and has done all the hard work of creating the language for us. It could be equally effective if a department were to give their own codified name to a particular technique they wanted to implement, as long as every member of the department is aware of the technique associated with the name.

Practice makes permanent

> 'Teaching is a performance profession… Just like the soccer player going for the goal, the actor delivering the monologue, and the surgeon performing an emergency operation, teachers have to deliver excellent instruction live: not only delivering on a great lesson plan but also modifying it swiftly and surely in response to whatever challenge or triumphs the pupils bring to the classroom that day.' (Bambrick-Santoyo, 2016, p. 25)

Imagine you watch this classroom exchange.

Teacher: How do we simplify $x^3 \times x^3 \times y \times y^2$?
Pupil: Add the indices.
Teacher: Well done; where the bases are the same, we can add the indices.

Here the teacher has 'rounded up' (another Lemov code) the pupil's answer. The pupil did not include the part about the bases needing to be the same, yet they were congratulated as having a correct response. In fact, the fully correct response was the teacher's work, but the pupil got the credit. An action step using shared language might look like this, 'During questioning, use "Right is right" by holding out for all-the-way right responses. Use responses, such as, "Good start, (name). Can you develop your answer?" ' Once a teacher understands 'Right is right' and all the ways they can address this, you can then just say, *'Practise "Right is right" in your next lesson,'* and be understood.

The next step is the practice itself. As we discussed earlier, habits take time and practice to change, and new habits take time and practice to form. To practise *'Right is right'* a teacher could rehearse imaginary classroom scenarios, with or without their coach, so that they are more likely to remember what to do in front of their actual class. They should not stop the practice after the first run but should be confronted with 'what if' scenarios once they get better at it. In the case above, you could ask, *'What if the pupil doesn't know the information required to develop their answer? What will you do?'*

Scripting is another effective way to improve a teacher's practice. Suppose a teacher needs support with removing filler words and redundant information from their exposition. Scripting the exposition with the teacher would develop their practice, pointing out which phrases could be communicated more succinctly and which redundant words could be removed.

Conscious competence

The best teachers don't always make the best coaches – this is because often the techniques they deploy have become so embedded into their practice they have become second nature, requiring little or no thought to action in the classroom. People who have been driving a long time often notice they get somewhere without being able to recall any of their journey. The driving process has become so automated that they don't give it conscious attention. Similarly, when you have been teaching a long time, the techniques you effectively use in the classroom will likely be subconscious. As brilliant as this is, other teachers observing you can leave your classroom feeling like the teaching they have just seen is unattainable for them, as if things happened for you like magic.

To get better at delivering feedback you will need to be consciously competent. This means being aware of what makes you a good teacher and identifying the techniques that you use which can be replicated for success by other practitioners. The techniques that you use need to be broken down into granular steps, so you can share with others and clearly measure their success step by step.

Chapter Summary

Throughout this chapter we have considered the ways in which we as leaders can develop our team. To be effective these actions and behaviours need to take place repeatedly, over time:

- Culture is too important to be left to chance. Communicate clearly and explicitly what you want to see from your team and model it every day.
- Remember the human first. Approach all interactions with compassion and empathy, and be humble enough to own it when you get it wrong.
- Take the time to get to know everyone in your team so that you can make effective use of their strengths, support them in improving their practice and give opportunities to develop towards their aspirations.
- Everyone in the team can and should be working to improve, including you.
- Feedback is a two-way conversation, but needs to have clarity to enable teachers to improve. A shared language and opportunity to practise supports this.
- Give feedback that is highest leverage, bite-sized, clear and measurable.

FURTHER READING

A thoughtful examination of the many subtle things which skilful leaders do and consider to get the very best from their teams is found in Mary Myatt's *High Challenge, Low Threat* (2016).

Adam Robbins' *Middle Leadership Mastery* (2021) is full of realistic expertise on all aspects of middle leadership, guided by perspectives from psychology and cognitive science.

In *Radical Candor* (2017), Kim Scott uses examples from her own successful career in the tech industry to illustrate how to create a culture of openness, where everyone strives to improve.

To develop a shared language around effective teacher behaviours, read Doug Lemov's *Teach Like a Champion 3.0* (2021). This book is a valuable tool for any teacher's own practice, but also for leaders who are supporting teacher development.

To learn about instructional coaching as a robust model for sustained teacher development, read Paul Bambrick-Santoyo's *Leveraging Leadership: A Practical Guide to Building Exceptional Schools* (2012) and Doug Lemov's *Practice Perfect: 42 Rules for Getting better at Getting Better* (2012).

Sam Crome's *Thriving Teams* (https://pocketwisdom.blog/category/thriving-teams) is a series of blogposts examining all aspects of thriving teams and how to establish them.

11

Some practicalities of leading a department

Leading a mathematics department is a tough but hugely rewarding job. We have responsibility for a core subject, double-counted on performance measures at GCSE, and our department teaches every pupil in the school. Getting it right means that scores of pupils leave our department each year with the mathematical knowledge and skills that will be truly empowering for their futures. This is a great responsibility and something that can be very fulfilling.

In this chapter we will explore the things you will encounter as the leader of a mathematics department that are over and above teaching and professional development; the things you might not even be aware happen until you start a role like this. By the time you have finished the chapter, and the book, we hope you feel equipped to be successful and know where to look next to learn even more.

The day-to-day minutiae

On top of the usual planning, teaching, assessment and feedback inherent in a standard mathematics teaching role, leading a team brings a whole host of extra responsibilities. These could include quality assurance of the department, curriculum planning, assessment design, data analysis and associated reporting and intervention planning, leading professional development for the team, setting cover work, following up on behaviour issues and communicating with parents. Ultimately we have a responsibility to improve teaching and learning, but how that manifests itself in the day-to-day nature of the job can be significantly influenced by the specifics of the context we are working in. Many heads of department feel that their to-do list grows exponentially. A high level of organisation is required if we are to be able to keep the main thing, the main thing.

An important part of leading a department is ensuring that the team have what they need to work effectively, removing barriers to this wherever possible. Establishing routines can make sure everything runs smoothly. For example, consider the difference between the way equipment is managed in the following departments:

Department A: Equipment is ordered in a haphazard way, as and when someone notices that something has run out. Teacher A wants to use mini-whiteboards to check their pupils' understanding, but always seems to be struggling to find enough board pens for the whole class. They feel as though it is always them that points out when equipment has run out and are reluctant to bother the head of department again. They tried asking other members of the team if they have any spare whiteboard pens as well but got a frosty reception since they interrupted another teacher's lesson. Rather than using the mini-whiteboards, they decide it is easier to just ask questions to a few pupils and hope that everyone else understands.

Department B: Teacher B has been delegated the task of keeping track of equipment levels and putting in any orders, approved by the head of department, so they can keep an eye on the budget. They have set up a spreadsheet which all members of the team can access to flag up when they are running low on something, which makes it easier for them to know what to order. Additionally, everyone in the department knows who to speak to about equipment orders, freeing up the head of department to focus on improving teaching and learning.

This is one example of a routine that makes teachers' lives easier and has a positive impact on pupils' experiences. Having clear routines in place for things that we can predict, such as ordering equipment, setting cover work or printing assessments, helps the department to function like a well-oiled machine. In this kind of department, when the unexpected happens, everyone is better placed to be able to tackle it and, in the day to day, the team is enabled to spend more of their time focusing on planning and delivering high-quality lessons. Part of the job of a leader is to create the conditions necessary for their team to do a good job. In the previous chapter, we considered this from the perspective of creating the right culture and environment for staff development, but we must also stay aware of any operational issues getting in the way and do what we can to mitigate or remove them.

Clear communication

Schools are complex organisations; an awful lot can take place in just one day and nobody can know absolutely everything that is going on. However, if teachers feel that communication is poor, particularly if a lack of timely information has left them in a tricky situation with a pupil, parent or colleague, or unable to meet a deadline, then this will have a negative impact on their job satisfaction. We need to carefully consider what, how and when we communicate information so that it is received clearly and acted on appropriately.

Email

In *Stop Talking About Wellbeing* (2020), Kat Howard explains that email can appear to be teachers' favourite form of communication, proving convenient when they are unable to leave their classrooms for much of the day, but it can also be a source of stress. A particular issue she highlights is that people feel compelled to check emails as soon as they arrive, even if they know that they are not actually required to do so. Such a compulsion can lead to teachers reading emails that enforce deadlines whilst they are at home, or checking emails during lessons when we would rather they give their full attention to the pupils in front of them. The urge to check emails as soon as they arrive can also lead to distractions from other work that requires our full attention, such as planning sequences of learning, meaning such tasks take significantly longer than they need to. Howard suggests that before sending emails we ask ourselves, *'Is this sent to the right person, at the right time, giving the right timescale for the right reason? How would it feel to be the recipient of this email?'*

Many schools now have email policies in place specifying times when emails should *not* be sent, and other aspects of email etiquette. Whether a school has such a policy in place or not, it can still be worthwhile considering the following:

- **Timing** – Will this be received at a time when the recipient can act on it effectively?

- **Tone** – Will this be read in the intended tone? Is there a risk of it being taken the wrong way?

- **Clarity** – Will the key message be understood?

- **Recipients** – Do you really need to reply all? Alternatively, is everyone who needs to see this included?

- **Length** – Is it realistic for the reader to read and take it all in?

There are certainly times when it is far more effective and efficient to find someone in person for a conversation rather than sending an email. If an email is likely to turn into a back-and-forth, a conversation would almost always be better and develops far more rapport. Sometimes, key people in the school building are more likely to respond quickly and helpfully to the leader who has taken the time to come and speak to them in person occasionally, than the one who only ever sends emails making demands. The bank balance of goodwill mentioned in Chapter 10 is not just reserved for those in your department!

Digital alternatives

During the pandemic, many schools made increased use of tools such as Microsoft Teams or Google Meet for online teaching and for communication and organisation. These tools have channels which you can set up for year groups or themes, such as assessment or reporting. Teachers can be added to relevant channels only to avoid a deluge of irrelevant information. The instant messaging in these systems can be more efficient than email, allowing people to *'like'* messages to acknowledge them. Many of these tools also have task boards – like an online pinboard – where you can assign tasks to individuals, with deadlines, and they can tick them off once done.

Some departments have their own instant messaging group using phone-based apps such as WhatsApp. Although these are often intended to be used socially, they can end up blurring the lines between school and home, sometimes becoming an alternative to sending work emails outside work hours. Howard describes WhatsApp as *'the department you can never leave'*, so if you decide to have a group like this, it is worthwhile establishing ground rules such as:

- No obligation to be part of the group or reply.

- There will be times when people want to mute the group and that is OK.

- No work chat outside of work hours (or perhaps no work chat at all, but make sure the team know how to contact you about urgent work issues outside of work hours when they arise).

Meetings and bulletins

Throughout this book we have talked about how precious time together as a mathematics department is. Ideally, we want to protect this time for genuine professional development as far as possible. However, there are a great many things we need to communicate to our teams, which may include key messages from meetings with our own line manager or meetings with other middle leaders and the senior team. In order to preserve departmental time for professional development, many heads of department share key messages via a regular 'housekeeping' email or bulletin sent to the whole team (you can find specific information and examples from various heads of mathematics on a Twitter thread started by Dani Quinn in 2020). This could include:

- sections for messages regarding each year group or key stage

- calendar items flagging up important dates coming up

- links to resources the team might find useful, especially for topics coming up soon on the scheme of work

- suggestions of helpful blogs, books or other sources of CPD

- admin reminders

- staff shout-outs

- mathematics puzzles.

As the week goes on and you think of things you need to let the department know about, add them to a draft email or a shared document, and send it out at a fixed, predictable point every week. Bearing in mind that the purpose of such a bulletin is to keep the department informed without eating into departmental time, we need to be sure that everyone will read the bulletin every time. Using departmental time to check that everyone has read and understood the bulletin somewhat defeats its purpose. We must therefore make explicit the expectation that all members of the department read the bulletin and that this is necessary, so that valuable department time can be used for developing everyone in the team. To ensure that a bulletin streamlines departmental communication, any responsibility holders in the team should be able to add information to it rather than sending separate emails.

Any department meeting should have an agenda and you should stick to it as much as possible. Make sure the team know that meeting time is focused on what needs doing, that they should not use it for general chit-chat or for discussions that might hog time or make things run over. If someone wants to discuss something in 'any other business' (AOB) they should try and let you know in advance where possible. Always remember that your teachers' time is limited and precious, so you should not take it unfairly or unnecessarily.

Predicting the predictable

Even the best leaders will find themselves dealing with sudden and unexpected challenges, but a well-run department should not have to fight fires unless they genuinely could not have been predicted. This means that when the unexpected happens, we have far greater capacity to manage it in a way that seems seamless to others. It is important to keep the team informed of important dates that are coming up to assist them with managing their time sensibly, however, a skilled leader needs to have a broader overview so that they can see potential pinch points before they occur. Often these will include items which should be visible to all on a whole-school calendar, but it can also be worthwhile keeping a department calendar highlighting dates and events likely to impact on the team. The exact nature of demands arising from some calendar items will differ depending on the context of the school, so it is important to check what is expected if unsure.

Assessment weeks

These throw up a whole host of associated deadlines and responsibilities. Make sure you know who is responsible for printing exam papers, organising and sharing seating plans, setting up exam venues and invigilating mock exams. Is there a system of quality assurance of assessments in the school? Do they need to be sent to a member of the senior team prior to the assessment week? What are the expectations regarding marking and data entry resulting from the assessments? Will we need to analyse the data prior to a data meeting with the senior team, or complete a data report explaining next steps?

The answers to these questions differ from school to school so it is important to know what the expectations are and any deadlines resulting from them. Knowing this will make things run more smoothly and allow us to pre-empt busy periods for ourselves and the team. If we have the opportunity to create buffers around these busy times then we should.

Open evenings

These are normally calendared far in advance. We must be mindful that, as well as the evening itself being demanding on staff, there can be lots of advance organisation involved. In some schools there may be events for pupils during the day as well as an evening, having knock-on implications for the usual timetabled lessons.

Open-evening activities need to be planned in advance. They do not have to be elaborate (in fact, there is an argument to say that they should be as close to what happens on a day-to-day basis as possible), but we must consider exactly what needs to be organised, and by whom, far enough in advance for it to be practical. Try not to arrange non-routine events for the week of an open evening – a series of surprise learning walks taking place the morning after is unlikely to be seen as supportive of the team's wellbeing.

Parents evenings

These generally require less prior organisation than an open evening, but still need to be flagged up well in advance. Where there is key information that all parents/carers should receive, it can be beneficial to put together an information sheet to hand out, with information about the course pupils are following, how it is assessed, useful websites and any key dates they should know. A standard sheet can be amended to fit year groups as necessary.

INSET days/whole-school professional development

INSET days should be easily identifiable in advance, but it still worthwhile reminding teachers of the dates, especially those that fall in the middle of a term rather than at the very start or end. Dates for whole-school professional development sessions are not always as well defined far in advance and are more likely to be subject to last-minute changes.

However, for both INSET days and whole-school professional development sessions, the more information we can have about the focus in advance, the better. As a head of department there is a possibility of being asked to contribute to sessions, or to lead discussion with the team at various points. Forewarning of the focus can lead to forward-planning and greater opportunities for the team to fully benefit from the time spent here.

Exam dates

It goes without saying that we need to have an eye on exam dates for our own subject, but it can also be a good idea to find out when other subjects have exams, as this can mean pupils missing their mathematics lessons. For example, pupils who study art or graphics will often need to spend a couple of days completing larger pieces of work prior to the main exam period. Some applied subjects might have exams in January, or have a requirement for controlled assessments that result in a group of pupils being absent from their normal lessons for a chunk of time. If the department is aware of any of these in advance it means that they can plan for it, minimising their negative impact on the pupils in class.

Enrichment events

In Chapter 6 we looked at different ways to enrich pupils' learning. Some of the ideas suggested take the form of competitions, events or trips, all of which lead to an element of disruption from normal lessons. Some of these, like UKMT Maths Challenges, take place at similar times each year and can be planned for with predictability. Enrichment events can be easily delegated to others in the team, with the head of department maintaining an overview. It is essential to keep an eye on any trips run by other departments that will impact on pupil attendance to mathematics lessons and ensure the rest of the department are also aware. Flag such events in your bulletin.

Delegation and balance

Leaders cannot and should not try to do everything in a department themselves. We do need to ensure that everything is done by somebody, we do need to have a good overview of the work being done, and we do need to quality-assure it. Many leaders find that they are very busy yet struggle to delegate tasks from their to-do list to others in the department, even when members of their team are eminently capable of supporting them and are even paid extra to do so.

Delegation can be difficult when you misunderstand roles. It is not your job to do everything in the department. It is not a teacher's job to only teach lessons and nothing else. Things like coordinating enrichment activities are well within the remit of a teacher and it is the leader's job to ensure these things happen well, using those in their team to their strengths. Sometimes a leader can be worried about putting extra stress onto busy teachers. If this is the case, we should focus our efforts on streamlining teacher's roles through, for instance, providing shared resources and taking away unnecessary workload like pointless marking (see Chapter 3). If we can free up some of teachers' time away from unnecessary or arduous work, we allow them to take on more enjoyable responsibilities.

Delegation is important for developing the skills of those in the department so that, one day, they are ready to take on positions of responsibility themselves if they so wish. This means we must be prepared that things will not always happen the way we would do them and accept that this is not necessarily a bad thing. Give people clear and achievable deadlines, support them along the way if they need it, and allow them to do a good job for you. A good leader will create a team full of people who are capable of moving on to promotion and, hopefully, an environment that means they don't want to!

Most of the reasons to delegate fall into one of three categories: developing the team, increasing motivation and buy-in, and effective time management.

Developing the team

As we saw in Chapter 10, a key duty of a head of department is to facilitate the improvement of everyone in their team. Part of this duty is about giving people opportunities to try something new and increase their experience in a variety of areas. As people get better at their job, they are able to make more informed decisions about where they see themselves in the future. Another part of this duty is succession management. In *High Challenge, Low Threat* (2016), Mary Myatt warns against the myth of hero leadership, stating that rather than trying to do everything alone, strong leaders regularly ask themselves, *'If I weren't here to do this work, what would happen? How would the organisation continue to thrive? What happens if I go away? How strong are the systems for continuing improvement?'* (p. 49).

Adam Robbins (2022) has noted that the role of head of department is somewhat subjective, with leaders able to morph it into whatever they are most interested in. If they like administration, it can become an admin role. If they like professional development, it becomes a staff development role. Due to this inherent role mutability, we need to build our team to ensure that everything that needs to happen still does. This is where delegation is essential.

Motivation and buy-in

Delegation and the monitoring of this allow other members of the team to build a fuller understanding of the departmental vision, the thought behind it, and insight into the barriers we face. Being assigned a task to complete for the benefit of the whole team can make a person feel more invested in and part of the team. It also demonstrates that they are trusted and can help them both feel more respected and feel more respect for the leader. Teachers who feel trusted and respected are more likely to feel empowered to make suggestions that could benefit the team, creating a department full of motivated people all invested in and supportive of each other. It may sound like a pipedream but it can be done if we create the right conditions.

Taking off the training wheels

Delegation does not necessarily mean giving someone a task and waiting for them to come back when it has been completed, especially not at first. Much as the type of feedback we give a teacher will depend on where they sit on the novice–expert spectrum, so there is also a spectrum of how directive we might be when delegating tasks depending on the level of expertise of the teacher taking on the task and the level of trust that has been built up.

If delegating to someone for the first time, or with a task they are new to, we might be fairly directive and hands on in guiding them as to how it should be done. As our trust in the teacher increases, and as their expertise increases, we are likely to shift towards being less directive, while leaving our door open so that we can be on hand if needed. Ultimately we must aim to become less and less directive as trust, confidence and expertise are built up. If we do not 'take off the training wheels', we risk being micro-managers. As Myatt explains, *'Sensible leaders catch themselves when they find themselves going into helicopter mode. It's tempting. We all care so much, we want things to go right. We know how to do it, it would save so much time. But the problem is that no one grows to their full potential if leaders are doing too much and if their colleagues feel they are being watched, stifled, not able to crack on.'* (2016, p. 95)

Delegation does not mean washing our hands of responsibility. Quality-assuring delegated work at a relatively early stage can be beneficial to give both us and the team greater security that they are doing the right things, resulting in swifter progress.

Working with our senior leaders

Every department leader will have a line manager on the senior leadership team, someone who acts as the conduit through which whole-school culture, policy and direction meets teachers in classrooms. Successful line management involves senior leaders understanding the specific requirements of the subject they are working with, and the head of department working with them to link the department to the rest of the school community.

Throughout this book we have tried to discuss general ideas through the lens of teaching mathematics. Mathematics, as a subject, can work very differently to others. Its hierarchical nature puts it in contrast to subjects like English or history, and closer in structure to science or languages, where knowledge explicitly and intrinsically builds on what has come before. Sometimes, these differences can result in mathematics leaders finding themselves at odds with whole-school policies and having to present the case of why something won't work to a (disbelieving) senior leader. It is certainly the case that some initiatives that work perfectly in one subject will fall flat on their face in mathematics, and a senior leader that understands this will be amenable to discussion.

It can be beneficial to be line-managed by someone from a different subject area than our own, as they can bring a different perspective and fresh ideas. Developing a trusting and productive relationship between line manager and head of department is far more important than aligning their subject areas. That said, a skilled head of department has a duty to protect their team from initiatives that may be unworkable in their subject area, but without being seen as negative and argumentative. At times this can feel as though it requires UN levels of tact and diplomacy, but it is essential to master 'managing up' to be effective in the role of head of department. Failing to do so at the right times can allow your team to waste valuable time and energy on projects that will have no impact on pupils' learning, and in some cases may even hinder it. Uncomfortable though it may feel at times, it is our responsibility to speak up when we know something is wrong.

If we are to avoid 'managing up' being seen as arguing or being negative, we must remember that the senior team are human too. Just as none of our team come into work wanting to do a bad job, our line managers want to do their best, for the pupils, staff and for you too. New initiatives are not introduced to make our lives more difficult, but because somebody thinks they will genuinely improve learning and pupil results. If we know that what is being asked of us is problematic in some way, it is our job to let our line manager know. If we know that something will not work for mathematics, it is not enough for us to just say that it will not work. We must explain clearly and calmly why it would not have the desired impact in mathematics, what the likely impact would be instead, and should provide evidence or other points of view to support our argument. It is always worth considering adjustments that could be made to an initiative that would make it more successful in mathematics, as this shows willing. However, if a watered-down version of a policy would still have the same negative impact then it is better to stand firm.

Sometimes a policy or initiative could have a sound basis, but you and the team are lacking something that you would need to be able to implement it effectively. It may be a brilliant idea for the pupils but would negatively impact on your team's workload in some way. If this is the case, ask for support from the senior team to implement it well – can something else be taken away, or can training be provided?

Line managers will have plenty of things they need to ask of heads of department but an important aspect of their role is to support and guide middle leaders and to help them by removing barriers at times. They can only do this if we communicate with them about what we need. We should always go into line management meetings well prepared, with a list of anything we need to discuss or flag up. Sometimes we might be able to explain exactly what we need to tackle a problem, sometimes we might need some help from them to find a solution, but either way the important thing is to tell them. Far better, for example, to explain that we are finding it difficult to find time to carry out learning walks in the department and work together on a solution, rather than say nothing due to not having a solution and then being asked why we have not been carrying out quality assurance of the team. What we are talking about here is openness, transparency and building trust, all elements that were important in building our team and which are relevant here too.

A productive working relationship between a head of mathematics and their line manager can take time to establish, but there are a few things we can do to help it along:

- Meet deadlines. If something is not going to be achievable, flag this up as early as possible, indicating what the issue is and when the task will be completed.

- Challenge in private. Wherever possible, iron out any issues with new policies *before* speaking to your department. When the department raises issues, be diplomatic, but it can be better to say you will seek clarification from the senior team, than to fall into public criticism of an initiative which only creates division.

- Be proactive. Try to look ahead and ask for any information you might need.

- Be honest. If something has gone wrong it is better to let them know yourself rather than have them find out from someone else.

- Be prepared for them to disagree with your solutions. They have a better idea of the whole-school picture.

- Be open to their suggestions. You may not always agree with them, but listening with an open mind helps to dispel any idea of you being negative.

- Understand how they work. What are their strengths and weaknesses? How do they communicate? You will not change them but you can adjust your approach.

- *'Anything else?'* If there is anything else you need to ask or tell them, then make sure you do. Much better to clarify anything during your meeting, than have to chase afterwards when they are busy with other things.

Working with other heads of subject

There may be times when mathematics leaders need to work with other subject leaders. Taking the time to form productive professional relationships can bring many benefits, as well as making our work more enjoyable. It can be helpful to share ideas or resources, collaborate on projects, or have a sounding board to discuss and vent with others when needed, so that when taking initiatives to the team we are able to do so in a positive way. It can be easy to feel like we are working in isolated silos unless we regularly reach out to contacts in other schools and subjects. However, there can also be times when we need to come to an agreement with other heads of department. Perhaps we need to agree on which pupils fall into which band, or decide on a common method to be used across mathematics and science, or a common exam board across a multi-academy trust. In such circumstances, having an established relationship can help, particularly if we understand how others work and what their motivations are. Developing professional sideways relationships can be the key to reaching swift consensus that meets the needs of pupils and staff.

Managing our time

Time is at an absolute premium for those leading a mathematics department. It can feel as though to-do lists grow at an exponential rate as there is always someone at the door needing *'just one thing...'* and every meeting leaves us with more tasks to complete and less time to do it in. Juggling the demands of the team, the pupils, SLT and the small matter of ensuring our own classes receive high-quality teaching can feel overwhelming. It is vital to organise and plan our time carefully. There are many ways to do this, but it can be helpful to consider the principles of the Eisenhower Matrix to support you.

	Urgent	Not Urgent
Important	**Do now** Tasks requiring immediate attention	**Do later** Tasks needing action, but not immediate attention
Not Important	**Delegate** Tasks requiring immediate action, that do not contribute to your goals	**Delete** Tasks that are neither urgent nor important

Considering what time we have to tackle our to-do list is helpful. Planning out when we will complete different tasks can ensure that the important things get done, or alert us to the fact that we may need to ask for help. Reviewing our to-do list at the end of each day and planning out what we will do the next day helps to minimise procrastination and clear our minds so that we are not spending all our time outside of work thinking about the job. In *60-Second CPD*, Hanna Beech and Ross Morrison McGill advocate the strategy of *'go hard and go home'* at some point each week. By this they mean making a list of short and easy tasks to complete at the end of a day, such as making a to-do list for the next day, tidying our desk or replying to an email and setting a timer for ten minutes to complete the tasks at the end of the day. Go home when the timer goes off, even if there are still tasks to complete. By ticking off some quick wins from the to-do list, we can feel a sense of accomplishment and often it is surprising what we can achieve in short, sharp bursts.

It is worthwhile letting the team know if we are leaving early. If they were hoping for a quiet word, they know to catch you at some other time (ideally scheduling this in with you) and, more importantly, it models to them the importance of not letting the job take over.

Setting a timer can be helpful at other times too. Kat Howard describes planning lessons as the *'comfort-blanket of teaching'*, which means it can end up taking more of our time than it needs to. For leaders it is even more important to remember that 'good enough' will do, and that time spent crafting the 'perfect' lesson might be better spent on other jobs that support the whole team, particularly if we find ourselves using lesson-planning as a form of procrastination to avoid a task we do not relish. Setting a time limit on our planning can help us to stay focused on good principles for planning, rather than dwelling on perfect presentation or reinventing the wheel. Some teachers make use of the Pomodoro Technique, named by Francesco Cirillo after a tomato-shaped timer used to track 25 minute bursts of focus followed by a five-minute break. There are a range of apps that allow a timer to be set for periods of focus time followed by short breaks for as many cycles as required.

Frog eating

Brian Tracy's book *Eat That Frog!* (2017) is full of productivity techniques, and although not specifically aimed at teachers, it has messages that all teachers can learn from. In Tracy's words,

'The first rule of frog eating is this:
*If you have to eat two frogs, eat the **ugliest** one first.*

The second rule of frog eating is this:
If you have to eat a live frog at all, it doesn't pay to sit and
look at it for very long.'

Essentially, even after prioritising, some tasks can end up languishing on our to-do lists as we procrastinate and try to avoid them. Often these 'frogs' are actually the tasks that would be the most valuable if we completed them quickly and well, but they also tend to be difficult and complex compared to others on our to-do lists. Tracy suggests getting the most awkward task out of the way early on so that it is not playing on our minds, impacting on our productivity. The 'frog' might be a difficult conversation with a member of the team, or a phone call home to a parent who has a reputation for being awkward. Consider the potential impact of delaying these. It never improves the situation.

Tracy discusses the Pareto principle, named after a nineteenth century Italian economist, which states that 20 per cent of tasks can give 80 per cent of value and it is these we should focus on, deleting or delegating ones that will not give the same returns. We have to consider that there is an opportunity cost to everything we choose to spend our time on and focus our efforts accordingly. Tracy also discusses the importance of carving out large chunks of time for bigger tasks. This can be incredibly difficult in the school day, but there are things we can do to protect large chunks of our planning time by limiting potential distractions. Be prepared in advance of these chunks of time so you can begin straight away, work somewhere you will not be disturbed and redirect potential distractions when a colleague comes to speak to you: *'I'm working on x now, but could we talk about it at y time?'* Single-handle every task, as humans are not as good at multitasking as we think. It is more efficient to focus on one task at a time until it is done, which may require us to break tasks into manageable chunks.

Chapter Summary

Throughout this chapter and the last, we have seen that a successful department depends on efficient systems and a leader that keeps a close eye on everything to ensure not only that things get done, but that their colleagues are given a workplace in which they can thrive. Ultimately, when a department runs smoothly and when teachers enjoy what they are doing, the ones who benefit the most are the pupils in our care.

- Keep the main thing the main thing by removing barriers where possible. Clear and timely communication, routines and automaticity can help.
- Preserve department time for professional development by moving key messages and admin to a weekly bulletin.
- Predict the predictable by having an overview of key dates impacting on the department's time and workload.
- Delegation is essential to the smooth running of a team and can enable others to develop professionally. However, we need to remember that we are still responsible for anything we delegate.
- We must also manage up and sideways at times. This does not mean manipulating situations to always get our own way. Professionalism and remembering our core moral purpose are key.

FURTHER READING

For practical strategies and case studies exploring workload and wellbeing in schools, read Kat Howard's *Stop Talking About Wellbeing* (2020). This book is useful for middle and senior leaders alike, jam-packed full of ways of ensuring work doesn't overtake everything else.

As a general guide to leading a department, Adam Robbins' *Middle Leadership Mastery* (2021) offers realistic expertise on all aspects of middle leadership, guided by perspectives from psychology and cognitive science.

A quick read packed with simple advice on how to avoid procrastination, Bryan Tracy's *Eat That Frog* (2017) helps you to manage your time more effectively.

References

Allen, R. and Sims, S. (2018), 'How do shortages of maths teachers affect the within-school allocation of maths teachers to pupils?', Nuffield Foundation, www.nuffieldfoundation. org/wp-content/uploads/2018/06/Within-school-allocati ons-of-maths-teachers-to-pupils_v_FINAL.pdf

Ausubel, D. P. (1968), *Educational Psychology: A cognitive view*. New York: Holt, Rinehart and Winston.

Bambrick–Santoyo, P. (with Peiser, B.) (2012), *Leverage Leadership: A practical guide to building exceptional schools*. San Francisco: Jossey-Bass.

Bambrick-Santoyo, P. (2016), *Get Better Faster*. San Francisco: Jossey-Bass.

Barton, C. (2018), *How I Wish I'd Taught Maths*. Woodbridge: John Catt Educational Ltd.

Barton, C. (2020), *Reflect, Expect, Check, Explain: Sequences and behaviour to enable mathematical thinking in the classroom*. Woodbridge: John Catt.

Beech, H. and Morrison McGill, R. (2020), *60-Second CPD: 239 ideas for busy teachers*. Woodbridge: John Catt.

Bellos, A. (2010), *Alex's Adventures in Numberland: Dispatches from the wonderful world of mathematics*. London: Bloomsbury Publishing.

Bennett, T. (2020), *Running the Room: The teacher's guide to behaviour*. Woodbridge: John Catt Educational.

Bentley-Davies, C. (2014), *How to be an Amazing Middle Leader*. Carmarthen: Crown House Publishing.

Bills, C., Bills, L., Watson, A. and Mason, J. (2018), *Thinkers: A collection of activities to provoke mathematical thinking*. Derby: Association of Teachers of Mathematics.

Björk, E. L. and Björk, R. A. (2011), 'Making things hard on yourself, but in a good way: creating desirable difficulties to enhance learning', in M. A. Gernsbacher, R. W. Pew, L. M. Hough and J. R. Pomerantz (eds), *Psychology and the Real World: Essays illustrating fundamental contributions to society*. New York: Worth Publishers, pp. 56–64.

Björk, R. A. and Björk, E. L. (1992), 'A new theory of disuse and an old theory of stimulus fluctuation', in A. F. Healy, S. M. Kosslyn and R. M. Shiffrin (eds), *Essays in Honor of William K. Estes, Vol. 2: From learning processes to cognitive processes*. Hillsdale, NJ: Lawrence Erlbaum Associates, pp. 35–67.

Brilliant.org (n.d.), 'Proofs of the Pythagorean Theorem', https://brilliant.org/wiki/proofs-of-the-pythagorean-theorem

Bruner, J. S. (1966), *Toward a Theory of Instruction*. Cambridge, MA: Harvard University Press.

Burkhardt, H. (2018), 'Ways to teach modelling – a 50 year study', *ZDM Mathematics Education*, 50, 61–75.

Christodoulou, D. (2017), *Making Good Progress? The future of Assessment for Learning*. Oxford: Oxford University Press.

Coe, R., Aloisi, C., Higgins, S. and Major, L. E. (2014), 'What makes great teaching? Review of the underpinning research', Sutton Trust, www.suttontrust.com/wp-content/uplo ads/2014/10/What-Makes-Great-Teaching-REPORT.pdf

Common Core State Standards Initiative (2022), 'Common Core State Standards for mathematics', https://learning.ccsso.org/wp-content/uploads/2022/11/ADA-Compliant-Math-Standards.pdf

Cooper, G. and Sweller, J. (1987), 'Effects of schema acquisition and rule automation on mathematical problem-solving transfer', *Journal of Educational Psychology*, 79, 347–362.

Counsell, C. (2018), 'Senior Curriculum Leadership 1: The indirect manifestation of knowledge: (A) curriculum as narrative', The Dignity of the Thing, https://thedignityofthethingblog.wordpr ess.com/2018/04/07/senior-curriculum-leadership-1-the-indir ect-manifestation-of-knowledge-a-curriculum-as-narrative

Crome, S. (2022a), Tweet, 29 August 2022, @Mr_Crome, https://twitter.com/Mr_Crome/status/1564344358991798279?s=20

Crome, S. (2022b), 'Thriving teams #3: psychological safety', Pocket Wisdom, https://pocketwisdom.blog/2022/01/08/thriving-teams-3-psychological-safety

Department for Education (DfE) (2021), 'National curriculum in England: mathematics programmes of study', https://www.gov.uk/government/publications/national-curriculum-in-england-mathematics-programmes-of-study/national-curriculum-in-england-mathematics-programmes-of-study

Didau, D. and Rose, N. (2016), *What Every Teacher Needs to Know about Psychology*. Woodbridge: John Catt.

Dienes, Z. P. (1961), *Building up Mathematics*. New York: Hutchinson Educational.

Dietiker, L. (2015), 'Mathematical story: a metaphor for mathematics curriculum', *Educational Studies in Mathematics*, 90, (3), 285–302.

Drury, H. (2014), *Mastering Mathematics: Teaching to transform achievement*. Oxford: Oxford University Press.

Eastaway, R. (2019), *Mathematics on the Back of an Envelope: Clever ways to (roughly) calculate anything*. Holmfirth: HarperCollins.

Eastaway, R. and Wyndham, J. (2005), *Why do Buses Come in Threes? The hidden maths of everyday life*. London: Portico.

Eastaway, R. and Wyndham, J. (2008), *How Long is a Piece of String? More hidden mathematics of everyday life*. London: Portico.

Ebbinghaus, H. (1885), *Memory: A contribution to experimental psychology*. New York: Dover.

Education Endowment Foundation (EEF) (n.d.(a)), 'Homework', https://educationendowmentfoundation.org.uk/education-evidence/teaching-learning-toolkit/homework

Education Endowment Foundation (EEF) (n.d.(b)), 'Life skills and enrichment', https://educationendowmentfoundation.org.uk/guidance-for-teachers/life-skills-enrichment

Education Endowment Foundation (EEF) (2018), 'Making best use of teaching assistants', https://educationendowmentfoundation.org.uk/education-evidence/guidance-reports/teaching-assistants

Engelmann, S. and Carnine, D. (2014), *Theory of Instruction: Principles and applications*. New York: Irvington Publishers.

Fletcher-Wood, H. (2018), *Responsive Teaching: Cognitive science and formative assessment in practice*. Abingdon: Routledge.

Gardiner, T. (2016), *Teaching Mathematics at Secondary Level*. Cambridge: Open Book Publishers.

Gatsby (2014), 'Good career guidance', www.gatsby.org.uk/educat ion/focus-areas/good-career-guidance

Gattengno, C. (1947–1963), *For the Teaching of Mathematics*, Educational Solutions Worldwide, https://issuu.com/eswi/docs/ fttomv1webbook; https://issuu.com/eswi/docs/fttomv2webb ook; https://issuu.com/eswi/docs/fttomv3webbook

Geary, D. (2007), 'Educating the Evolved Mind' in In J. S. Carlson and J. R. Levin (eds), *Educating the evolved mind: Conceptual foundations for an evolutionary educational psychology*. Greenwich, CT: Information Age, pp. 1–100.

Gilmore, C., Göbel, S. M. and Inglis, M. (2018), *An Introduction to Mathematical Cognition*. Abingdon: Routledge.

Große, C. and Renkl, A. (2004), 'Learning from worked examples: what happens if errors are included?', in P. Gerjets, J. Elen, R. Joiner and P. Kirschner (eds), *Instructional Design for Effective and Enjoyable Computer-Supported Learning*. Tübingen, Germany: Knowledge Media Research Center, pp. 356–64.

Halmos, P. (1980), 'The heart of mathematics', *The American Mathematical Monthly*, 87, (7), 519–24.

Halmos, P., Moise, E. and Piranian, G. (1975), 'The problem of learning to teach', *The American Mathematical Monthly*, 82, (5), 466–76.

Howard, K. (2020), *Stop Talking about Wellbeing*. Woodbridge: John Catt Educational Ltd.

Hua, H. (2022), Tweet, 19 August 2022, @howie_hua, https://twitter.com/howie_hua/status/1560431211717177 344?s=20&t=SMrV8AVN8BNRtqqQHiXcwQ

Kaput, J. (1987). Representation system and mathematics. In C. Janvier (ed), *Problems of representation in the teaching and learning of mathematics*. Hillsdale, NJ: Lawrence Erlbaum Associates, pp. 19–26.

Karpicke, J. D. and Roediger, H. L. III (2008), 'The critical importance of retrieval for learning', *Science*, 319, 966–68.

Lappan, G. and Briars, D. (1995), 'How should mathematics be taught?', in I. M. Carl (ed), *Seventy-Five Years of Progress: Prospects for school mathematics*. Reston, VA: The National Council of Teachers of Mathematics, pp. 131–56.

Lemov, D. (2021), *Teach Like a Champion 3.0*. San Francisco: Jossey-Bass.

Lemov, D., Woolway, E. and Yezzi, K. (2012), *Practice Perfect: 42 rules for getting better at getting better*. San Francisco: Jossey-Bass.

Lo Bello, A. (2013), *Origins of Mathematical Words: A comprehensive dictionary of Latin, Greek, and Arabic roots*. Baltimore, Maryland: John Hopkins University Press.

Mason, J., Burton, L. and Stacey, K. (2010), *Thinking Mathematically*. London: Pearson.

Mattock, P. (2019), *Visible Maths: Using representations and structure to enhance mathematics teaching in schools*. Carmarthen: Crown House Publishing.

McCourt, M. (2019), *Teaching for Mastery*. Woodbridge: John Catt Educational.

McCrea, E. (2019), *Making Every Maths Lesson Count: Six principles to support great maths teaching*. Carmarthen: Crown House Publishing.

McGrane, C. and McCourt, M. (2020), *Mathematical Tasks: The bridge between teaching and learning*. Woodbridge: John Catt Educational.

McNeil, N. M. and Alibali, M. W. (2005), 'Why won't you change your mind? Knowledge of operational patterns hinders learning and performance on equations', *Child Development*, 76, (4), 883–99.

Miller, G. (1956), 'The magical number seven, plus or minus two: some limits on our capacity for processing information', *The Psychological Review*, 63, 81–97.

Ministry of Education Singapore (2012), 'Mathematics syllabus: Primary One to Six', www.moe.gov.sg/-/media/files/primary/mathematics_syllabus_primary_1_to_6.pdf

Myatt, M. (2016), *High Challenge, Low Threat*. Woodbridge: John Catt Educational Ltd.

National Centre for Excellence in the Teaching of Mathematics (NCETM) (n.d.), 'Specialist knowledge for teaching mathematics (secondary non-specialist teachers) programme', www.ncetm.org.uk/maths-hubs-projects/specialist-knowledge-for-teaching-mathematics-secondary-non-specialist-teachers-programme

National Centre for Excellence in the Teaching of Mathematics (NCETM) (2022), 'Planning collaboratively and learning together as a department', www.ncetm.org.uk/features/planning-collaboratively-and-learning-together-as-a-department

Obersteiner, A., Van Dooren, W., Van Hoof, J. and Verschaffel, L. (2013), 'The natural number bias and magnitude representation in fraction comparison by expert mathematicians', *Learning and Instruction*, 28, 64–72.

Paas, F. and van Merriënboer, J. (1994), 'Variability of worked examples and transfer of geometrical problem-solving skills: a cognitive-load approach', *Journal of Educational Psychology*, 86, 122–33.

Paivio, A., Walsh, M. and Bons, T. (1994), 'Concreteness effects on memory: when and why?', *Journal of Experimental Psychology: Learning, Memory, and Cognition*, 20, 1196–204.

Parker, M. (2019), *Humble Pi: A comedy of mathematics errors*. London: Penguin.

Pershan, M. (2021), *Teaching Math with Examples*. Woodbridge: John Catt Educational.

Piaget, J. (1952), *The Origins of Intelligence in Children*. New York: W.W. Norton & Co.

Piaget, J. (1967), *Six Psychological Studies*. New York: Random House.

Pólya, G. (1945), *How to Solve It*. Princeton: Princeton University Press.

Quinn, D. (2020), Tweet, 16 October 2020, @danicquinn, https://twitter.com/danicquinn/status/1317068320986796 034?s=20&t=KAMHJfQs9XRGNqLV8AFznQ

Reimer, L. and Reimer, W. (1990), *Mathematicians are People, too: Stories from the lives of great mathematicians*. New York: Dale Seymour Publications.

Renkl, A. and Atkinson, R. (2003), 'Structuring the transition from example study to problem solving in cognitive skills acquisition: a cognitive load perspective', *Educational Psychologist*, 38, 15–22.

Rice, J. K. (2003), *Teacher Quality: Understanding the effectiveness of teacher attributes*. Washington DC: Economic Policy Institute.

Rittle-Johnson, B. and Schneider, M. (2015), 'Developing conceptual and procedural knowledge of mathematics', in R. Cohen Kadosh and A. Dowker (eds), *The Oxford Handbook of Numerical Cognition*. Oxford: Oxford University Press, pp. 732–44.

Robbins, A. (2021), *Middle Leadership Mastery*. Carmarthen: Crown House Publishing.

Robbins, A. (2022), Tweet, 20 July 2022, @MrARobbins, https://twitter.com/MrARobbins/status/1549653553211473 920?s=20&t=KAMHJfQs9XRGNqLV8AFznQ

Sani, N. and Burghes, D. (2021), 'Longitudinal study of "retraining" non-maths specialist teachers to become capable, confident teachers of mathematics', *International Journal of Mathematical Education in Science and Technology*, 53, (9), 2438–64.

Schneps, L. (2013), *Math on Trial: How numbers get used and abused in the courtroom*. New York: Basic Books.

Scott, K. (2017), *Radical Candor: How to get what you want by saying what you mean*. London: Pan Macmillan.

Sherrington, T. (2019a), *Rosenshine's Principles in Action*. Woodbridge: John Catt Educational.

Sherrington, T. (2019b), 'Signposting the hinterland: practical ways to enrich your core curriculum', Teacherhead, https://

teacherhead.com/2019/09/27/signposting-the-hinterland-practi
cal-ways-to-enrich-your-core-curriculum

Singh, S. (1997), *Fermat's Last Theorem*. London: Fourth Estate.

Singh, S. (1999), *The Code Book: The secret history of codes and
code-breaking*. London: Fourth Estate.

Singh, S. (2013), *The Simpsons and their Mathematics Secrets*.
London: Bloomsbury Publishing.

Sobel, D. and Alston, S. (2021), *The Inclusive Classroom: A new
approach to differentiation*. London: Bloomsbury Education.

Southall, E. (2022), *If I Could Tell You One Thing*. Leicester: The
Mathematical Association.

Stein, M. K. and Lane, S. (1996), 'Instructional tasks and the
development of pupil capacity to think and reason: an analysis
of the relationship between teaching and learning in a reform
mathematics project', *Educational Research and Evaluation*,
2, 50–80.

Swan, M. (2005), 'Improving learning in mathematics: challenges
and strategies', *Department for Education and Skills*, https://
colleenyoung.files.wordpress.com/2010/04/improving_learn
ing_in_mathematicsi.pdf

Sweller, J. (1994), 'Cognitive load theory, learning difficulty and
instructional design', *Learning and Instruction*, 4, (4), 295–312.

Sweller, J., Ayres, P. L., Kalyuga, S. and Chandler, P. A. (2003),
'The expertise reversal effect', *Educational Psychologist*, 38,
(1), 23–31.

Sweller, J., Clark, R. and Kirschner, P. (2010), 'Teaching general
problem-solving skills is not a substitute for, or a viable
addition to, teaching mathematics', *Notices of the American
Mathematical Society*, 57, (10), 1303–4.

Takahashi, A. (2021), *Teaching Mathematics Through
Problem Solving: A pedagogical approach from Japan*.
Abingdon: Routledge.

Tracy, B. (2017), *Eat That Frog!* London: Yellow Kite.

Turner, E., Goodwin, D. and Caviglioli, O. (2022), *Annie Murphy
Paul's The Extended Mind in Action*. Woodbridge: John Catt
Educational Ltd.

Van Merriënboer, J. J. G. and Kirschner, P. A. (2018), *Ten Steps to Complex Learning* (3rd edn). New York: Routledge.

What Works Clearinghouse (2018), 'Improving mathematical problem solving in Grades 4 through 8', https://ies.ed.gov/ncee/wwc/PracticeGuide/16

Wiliam, D. (2012), 'Every teacher can improve', YouTube, https://youtu.be/eqRcpA5rYTE

Wiliam, D. (2019), 'Teaching not a research-based profession', *TES Magazine*, 30 May 2019, www.tes.com/magazine/archive/dylan-wiliam-teaching-not-research-based-profession

Williams, T. (2018), *Power in Numbers: The rebel women of mathematics*. New York: Race Point Publishing.

Willingham, D. (2021), *Why Don't Students Like School? A Cognitive Scientist Answers Questions About How the Mind Works and What It Means for the Classroom*. San Francisco: Jossey-Bass.

Woodham, L. (2021), 'Using NRICH tasks to develop key problem-solving skills', https://nrich.maths.org/11082

Woodward, J., Beckmann, S., Driscoll, M., Franke, M., Herzig, P., Jitendra, A. et al. (2012), *Improving Mathematical Problem Solving in Grades 4 Through 8: A practice guide (NCEE 2012–4055)*. Washington, DC: National Center for Education Evaluation and Regional Assistance, Institute of Education Sciences, U.S. Department of Education.

Index

abstract versus concrete 91
adaptive teaching 78–83
Advanced Mathematics Support
    Programme (AMSP) 157,
    160, 162–3, 165, 211, 212
algebra tiles 105–7
area model 97–9
assessment weeks 264–5
Association of Teachers of
    Mathematics (ATM) 211
attention 36–8
authenticity 240–1

backward-looking methods 25
backwards-fading 80, 188
Bank of England 162
bar model 100–2
base ten blocks 104
Bletchley Park, Milton
    Keynes 161–2
blogs 213–14
books, significance of 155, 202
Bowland Mathematics 157

change, and personal
    development 204
choral response 59–60
classroom instructions
    attention 36–8
    communication 49–54
    example-problem pairs 38–9
    examples and
        definitions 60–3

exemplification 34–6
exercise books 56–7
explaining and
    questioning 39–42
gestures 63–5
live modelling in writing 55–6
non-standard examples 43
numbers, importance of 47–8
standard examples 43
using mistakes 44–6
vocabulary 57–60
coaching staff 250–1
cognitive load theory 173–7
    extraneous load 176–7
    germane load 177
    intrinsic load 175–6
coherence, lack of 205–6
collaboration 6–7
communication 49–54
communications 259–63
    digital alternatives 261–2
    email 260–1
    meetings and bulletins 262–3
competitions 164–5
Complete Maths 212
conceptual understanding
    89–91
conceptual understanding
    task 15
concrete and pictorial
    representations 187
concrete-pictorial-abstract (CPA)
    approach 91–3, 187

concrete representations 102–7, 109–12
  algebra tiles 105–7
  base ten blocks 104
  counters 103
  Cuisenaire rods 102–3
  place value counters 105
concrete versus abstract 91
conscious competence 253–4
cost barrier 204
counters 103
Cuisenaire rods 102–3
curricular thread/ number lines 113–18
curriculum 148, 217
  coherence 205–6, 223–33
  collective responsibility 231–3
  concept threads 223–5
  curricular threads 113–8, 231
  method threads 225–9
  representation threads 229–30
  sequencing and narrative 10–12, 218–22
cynicism 205

delegation and balance 267–8
desirable difficulty 182
Desmos software 158
Diagnostic Questions 44–5
Dienes blocks 104, 187
disciplinary knowledge 119
double number line and ratio tables 95–7
dual coding 186, 187

enriching learning 28
enrichment 147
  competitions 164–5
  events 162–3, 267
  funding 165–7

hinterland knowledge 148–9
history 149–51
in-house events 163–4
links to other topics 153
mathematical art 158
mathematics careers resources 160–1
mathematics clubs 157–8
puzzles and games 159–60
questions and tasks 157
sources 154–67
trips 161–2
visual proofs and demonstrations 151–2
escape rooms 164
Espressos newsletter 210
events 162–3
evidence-informed teaching 208–10
evolutionary psychology 172–3
exam dates 266
examiner, becoming an 202
examiner reports 202
example-problem pairs 38–9
exemplification 34–6
exercise books 56–7
exit tickets 76–7
expanding two brackets 23–4, 25
expertise reversal effect 188
explaining and questioning 39–42

F1 in schools competition 165
face-to-face courses 211
fear of failure 204–5
feedback 85–6
flexibility of knowledge 124–6
forgetting curve 190
formative assessment 68–78
forward-looking methods 25

frog eating 276–7
funding 165–7

general pedagogical
      knowledge 202–3
Geogebra 181
gestures 63–5
grid method 25
guidance fading effect 188

hinge questions 73–4
hinterland knowledge 148–9
homework 29–30

in-house events 163–4
inline presentation 25
inquiry 141–4
inquiry prompts 142–3
INSET days/whole-
      school professional
      development 266
*Inspiring Tomorrow's
      Engineers* 161
Institute of Mathematics and its
      Applications (IMA) 160
Interwoven Maths 222
Islamic art 158

Jodrell Bank Observatory 162

kakuro 159
knowledge 172

language 26–7
leading department
   assessment weeks 264–5
   communications 259–63
   day-to-day minutiae 257–9
   delegation and balance 267–8
   developing team 268–70
   enrichment events 267

exam dates 266
frog eating 276–7
INSET days/whole-
      school professional
      development 266
open evenings 265
parents evenings 265
time management 274–6
working with other heads of
      subject 274
working with senior
      leaders 270–4
learning, significance of 5
live modelling in writing 55–6
long-term memory 188–91

manipulatives 109–13
marking 85
mathematical art 158
Mathematical Association
      (MA) 210–11
mathematical cognition 193–4
mathematical thinking 119–21
   mathematical
      understanding 121–4
   practice 124–6
mathematics careers
      resources 160–1
mathematics clubs 157–8
Mathematics Education
      Innovation (MEI) 212–13
Mathematics Feasts 165
Mathematics Outreach
      Teams 163
Mathematics Roadshow 164
mathematics subject
      associations 212
Mathematics Week
      England 163
*Math Games With Bad
      Drawings* (Orlin) 159

Maths City, Leeds 161
MathsConfs 212
Maths Inspiration shows
162–3
MathsJam 156
misconceptions, avoid or
reduce 13, 73–4
mistakes 44–6
modelling cycle 141–2
motivation theory 173
multiple-choice questions
(MCQs) 72–3, 75
multiple representations
107–8
Museum of Science and
Industry, Manchester 162

National Centre for Excellence
in the Teaching of
Mathematics (NCETM) 211
National Cipher Challenge 165
natural number bias 194
Neon 161
non-standard examples 43
non-verbal communication 63–5
NRICH 157, 164
NSPCC Number Day 163
number line 94–5
numbers, importance of 47–8

online courses 212
open evenings 265
Open Middle 157
Ormiston Academies
Trust's MathOlympics
competitions 166–7

paid conferences 212–13
paid memberships 210–11
Parallel Project (Singh) 159
parents evenings 265

Pareto principle 277
personal professional
development
barriers 203–6
evidence-informed
teaching 208–10
face-to-face courses 211
general pedagogical
knowledge 202–3
mathematics-specific
pedagogical
knowledge 201–2
online courses 212
paid conferences 212–13
paid memberships 210–11
reflective practice 206–8
social media 213–14
sources of 210–14
subject knowledge
199–200
physical manipulatives 111
pictorial representations
94–102, 109–12
area model 97–9
bar model 100–2
double number line and ratio
tables 95–7
number line 94–5
place value tables 99–100
Pi day 164
place value counters 105
place value tables 99–100
planning learning
collaboration 6–7
enriching learning 28
homework 29–30
language 26–7
mathematics-specific
pedagogical knowledge 8
misconceptions, avoid or
reduce 13

pupil's participation and thinking 16–21
with questioning 12
representations and methods 21–5
resources 30–1
self-questioning 8–9
storytelling 10–12
subject knowledge 7–8
tasks 14–16
podcasts 155–6, 202, 213
polysemous words 57–8
praise 80
pre-tests 69
primary knowledge, biologically 172
Pringles 158
problem-solving 132–41
problem-solving task 15
procedural fluency task 14–15
professional reflection 201–2
pupil's participation and thinking 16–21
puzzles and games 159–60

question-level analysis (QLA) 235

reasoning ability 126–32
reflective practice 206–8
representations 35–6
representing mathematics
algebra tiles 105–7
area model 97–9
bar model 100–2
base ten blocks 104
conceptual understanding 89–91
concrete-pictorial-abstract (CPA) approach 91–3
concrete representations 102–7, 109–12

counters 103
Cuisenaire rods 102–3
curricular thread/ number lines 113–18
double number line and ratio tables 95–7
manipulatives 109–13
multiple representations 107–8
number line 94–5
pictorial representations 94–102, 109–12
place value counters 105
place value tables 99–100
ResearchEd conferences 212
responsive teaching 67
adaptive teaching 78–83
curriculum and planning 68
feedback 85–6
formative and summative assessment 68–78
teaching assistants 83–4
retrieval practice 209

schema 123, 188, 190
School Escape Rooms 164
science and research
cognitive load theory 173–7
concrete and pictorial representations 187
dual coding 186
evolutionary psychology 172–3
expertise reversal effect 188
guidance fading effect 188
long-term memory 188–91
mathematical cognition 193–4
spacing 191–2
split-attention effect 182–6

testing effect 192–3
worked example 177–82
scripting 253
secondary knowledge,
    biologically 172–3
self-questioning 8–9
SET (card game) 159
shared approaches, significance
    of 21–3
shared language
    techniques 251–2
Sieve of Eratosthenes 18–20
social media 213–14
spacing 191–2
specialist 245
split-attention effect 182–6
standard examples 43
STEM ambassadors 161
STEM club 157
Steward, Don 157
storytelling 10–12
strategies, analysis of 140
subject knowledge 7–8,
    199–200
substantive knowledge
    119
sudoku 159–60
summative assessment 68–78,
    234–7, 264–5

teaching assistants 83–4
team development 268–9
    authenticity of leadership 242
    coaching staff 250–1
    conscious competence 253–4
    feedback 248–50
    lessons observations 247–8

motivation and buy-in 269
non-specialists in 245–7
openness and safety, culture
    of 242–5
practice 252–3
shared language
    techniques 251–2
team culture 240–1
trainings 269–70
testing effect 192–3
theme parks 162
thinking
    and participation 16–21
Think Mathematics 158
Think Pair Share 60
time management 203–4,
    274–6
trips 161–2
Twitter 155, 214

UKMT Maths Challenges 267
United Kingdom Mathematics
    Trust (UKMT) 164
universal free schooling 172

visual representations
    140
vocabulary 57–60

WhatsApp 261–2
White Rose Maths 212
worked example 177–82

yohaku 159
YouTube Channels 155

zoos 162